UNITED STATES DEPARTMENT OF COMMERCE • Alexander B. Trowbridge, *Secretary*
NATIONAL BUREAU OF STANDARDS • A. V. Astin, *Director*

Tables of Bimolecular Gas Reactions

A. F. Trotman-Dickenson* and G. S. Milne*

*Prepared under contract at the
Edward Davies Chemical Laboratory
Aberystwyth, Wales

NSRDS-NBS 9
National Standard Reference Data Series-
National Bureau of Standards 9

(Category 6—Chemical Kinetics)

Issued October 27, 1967

For sale by the Superintendent of Documents, U.S. Government Printing Office
Washington, D.C. 20402 - Price $2 (Buckram)

Library of Congress Catalog Card Number: 67–60026

Foreword

The National Standard Reference Data System is a government-wide effort to give to the technical community of the United States optimum access to the quantitative data of physical science, critically evaluated and compiled for convenience. This program was established in 1963 by the President's Office of Science and Technology, acting upon the recommendation of the Federal Council for Science and Technology. The National Bureau of Standards has been assigned responsibility for administering the effort. The general objective of the System is to coordinate and integrate existing data evaluation and compilation activities into a systematic, comprehensive program, supplementing and expanding technical coverage when necessary, establishing and maintaining standards for the output of the participating groups, and providing mechanisms for the dissemination of the output as required.

The NSRDS is conducted as a decentralized operation of nation-wide scope with central coordination by NBS. It comprises a complex of data centers and other activities, carried on in government agencies, academic institutions, and nongovernmental laboratories. The independent operational status of existing critical data projects is maintained and encouraged. Data centers that are components of the NSRDS produce compilations of critically evaluated data, critical reviews of the state of quantitative knowledge in specialized areas, and computations of useful functions derived from standard reference data.

For operational purposes, NSRDS compilation activities are organized into seven categories as listed below. The data publications of the NSRDS, which may consist of monographs, loose-leaf sheets, computer tapes, or any other useful product, will be classified as belonging to one or another of these categories. An additional "General" category of NSRDS publications will include reports on detailed classification schemes, lists of compilations considered to be Standard Reference Data, status reports, and similar material. Thus, NSRDS publications will appear in the following eight categories:

Category	*Title*
1	General
2	Nuclear Properties
3	Atomic and Molecular Properties
4	Solid State Properties
5	Thermodynamic and Transport Properties
6	Chemical Kinetics
7	Colloid and Surface Properties
8	Mechanical Properties of Materials

Within the National Bureau of Standards publication program a new series has been established, called the National Standard Reference Data Series. The present report, which is in Category 6 of the above list, is Number 9 of the new series and is designated NSRDS–NBS 9.

A. V. ASTIN, *Director.*

Contents

Tables of Bimolecular Gas Reactions

A. F. Trotman-Dickenson and G. S. Milne

This survey covers the kinetics of bimolecular and termolecular gas reactions that do not involve atoms or molecules in electronically excited states. Bimolecular reactions are here defined as reactions in which two molecules are involved as reactants, that yield two or more molecules as products. Those reactions in which two molecules combine to form one molecule are most usefully considered as the reverse of unimolecular reactions which will be dealt with in another survey. Reactions of oxygen and nitrogen atoms have been omitted as they will also form the subject of another survey.

The literature from 1954 to December 31, 1965 has been exhaustively searched and it is hoped that for this period nothing has been omitted that should have been included.

The survey of earlier work has been based on one of the writers' books on "Gas Kinetics" which covered the literature to 1954. Use of the book for over ten years has revealed few omissions and these have been included in these tables. Data for the period January to August 1966 has been included where possible.

Key Words: Chemical kinetics, gas, bimolecular, reactions, tables, rate constants, activation energies, Arrhenius equation, data.

Preface

This survey covers the kinetics of bimolecular and termolecular gas reactions that do not involve atoms or molecules in electronically excited states. Bimolecular reactions are here defined as reactions in which two molecules are involved as reactants, that yield two or more molecules as products. Those reactions in which two molecules combine to form one molecule are most usefully considered as the reverse of unimolecular reactions which will be dealt with in another survey. Reactions of oxygen and nitrogen atoms have been omitted as they will also form the subject of another survey.

The literature from 1954 to December 31, 1965 has been exhaustively searched and it is hoped that for this period nothing has been omitted that should have been included.

The survey of earlier work has been based on one of the writers' books on "Gas Kinetics" which covered the literature to 1954. Use of the book for over ten years has revealed few omissions and these have been included in these tables. Data for the period Janaury to August 1966 has been included where possible.

Originally it was hoped to make this survey a critical study from which reliable data could be distilled. As the work proceeded it became evident that this was not a realistic goal. Only a small fraction of the reactions has been the subject of investigation by several workers. When several studies have been made the results fall into two classes. In the first class are those reactions that have been repeatedly investigated. It is then usually found that the discrepancies are greater than the random errors and that some systematic differences exist. It is not possible to decide which value is most nearly correct. In the second class are those reactions that have been investigated under widely different conditions. In these cases the best result for one purpose may not be the best for another, so that no useful choice can be made. We therefore decided to make the tables as comprehensive as possible so that users can readily discover what information is available.

It is likely that some reactions have been omitted and that other errors have crept in. We shall be grateful if readers will write to tell us of suggested improvements. It is hoped to publish supplements to these tables every two or three years.

Notes on the Tables

All the rate data is in the simple Arrhenius form $k=Ae^{-E/RT}$. "A" factors and rate constants are in cm. mole. sec. units throughout. Activation energies are in kcal/mole and temperatures in degrees centigrade.

Where data has been represented by equations of the type

$$k=BT^{n}e^{-H/RT} \qquad \left(n=1,\frac{1}{2},\frac{1}{4}\right),$$

B and H have been converted to the simple form by means of the equations

$$A=e^{n}BT^{n} \text{ and } E=H+nRT,$$

where T is the absolute temperature at the mid-point of the experimental range.

Where the rate equation is reported as a more complex function of temperature, it has been quoted as such in the tables.

Most of the data is for simple radical/molecule metathetical reactions of the type

$$R_1+R_2X=R_1X+R_2$$

where R_1 is an atom or radical attacking a molecule R_2X. X is the atom transfered in the reaction.

For each radical R_1 there is a separate table (see contents). The first column of each table consists of a list of molecules R_2X with which R_1 reacts. Columns three to five contain the Arrhenius values and the experimental temperature ranges. Column six gives an indication of the nature of the experimental method used to obtain the data.

The following abbreviations have been used in describing the radical source:

P	photolysis.
F.P.	flash photolysis
T	thermal reaction
S.T.	shock tube
D.F.	diffusion flame
M.D.F.	modified diffusion flame
M.L.	mean life method
Dil. F.	dilute flame
M.B.	molecular beam
+H	Hg photosensitized addition of H atoms to olefines.
−H	Hg photosensitized removal of H atoms from saturated compounds.
$+CH_3$	CH_3 radical attack on the parent compound.

The other radical source abbreviations used, such as H_2/discharge and H_2/O_2 flame, are self explanatory.

The table for each attacking species R_1 is split into six sections defined by the atom X being transferred. In the order used in the tables these are:
(i) hydrogen atom transfer
(ii) fluorine atom transfer
(iii) chlorine atom transfer
(iv) bromine atom transfer
(v) iodine atom transfer
(vi) oxygen atom transfer

Only in the case of methyl radicals are all six categories used.

In the few cases not covered by this classification e.g., transfer of an atom from the radical to the molecule as in

$$HO_2+CO=CO_2+OH,$$

either the reaction is written in full, or the products of the reaction are indicated in a footnote.

A seventh category of reactions not already covered (e.g., group transfer and inversion reactions) is included at the end of each table.

Simple ratios of rate constants (of the form k_1/k_2) are presented in separate tables, these proved much more difficult to classify, and wherever necessary, explanations of the construction of these tables are included at the head of the table.

Rate data is available in the literature as complex functions of several rate constants: this data has not been included, but references as to where it is available are given at the appropriate sections in the tables.

Where data is considered to be doubtful this is indicated in a footnote. As far as possible, an attempt has been made to include criticism of data by cross reference. Thus, where several references are given for one set of Arrhenius values, the first reference contains the values themselves; the other references indicate the sources of supplementary data and/or comment on the values shown.

Where a sufficient quantity of data has been collected for any one reaction, recommended Arrhenius values are given. They are compatible in all cases with the values for the reverse reaction (where these are known).

List of Tables

List of Tables—Continued

2. Radicals Containing One Carbon Atom—Continued

3. Radicals Containing Two Carbon Atoms

4. Radicals Containing Three Carbon Atoms

5. Radicals Containing Four Carbon Atoms

6. Miscellaneous Carbon-Containing Radicals

7. Inorganic Radicals

8. Radical–Radical Reactions

9. Molecule–Molecule Reactions

10. Odds and Ends

Reaction of Hydrogen Atoms

Index

Metathetical Reactions of Hydrogen Atoms With Hydrogen

Reactions	Notes	E	$\log_{10} A$	Temperature range	Radical source	Reference
		(kcal mole^{-1})	*(cm^3 mole^{-1} sec^{-1})*	°C		
$H+H_2$	(a)	6.68	13.78			1
	(b)	7.5 ± 1	13.7	10–730		2
	(d) (c)	8.0 ± 0.5	14.05	10–730		8
		$\log_{10} k = 15.45 - 3.49 \times 10^3/T + 3.84 \times 10^5/T^2$		27–171	H_2/tungsten spiral	11
	(e) (f)	$k = 1.18 \times 10^{15} T^{-1/2} \Gamma \exp(-9.21 \times 10^3/RT)$		27–171	H_2/tunsgten spiral	12
$H+\mathbf{H}D$	(a)	6.96	13.12			1
$H+H\mathbf{D}$	(a)	7.04	13.06			1
$H+D_2$	(a)	7.48	13.32			1
		7.30 ± 0.1	12.64 ± 0.05	95–195	H_2/tungsten spiral	13
$D+H_2$	(a)	6.14	13.37			1
	(f)	$k = 3.63 \times 10^{15} T^{-1/2} \Gamma \exp(-9.4[illegible] \times 10^3/RT)$		1–195	D_2/tungsten spiral	12
$D+\mathbf{H}D$	(a)	6.40	12.99			1
$D+H\mathbf{D}$	(a)	6.48	12.93			1
$D+D_2$	(a)	6.09	13.49			1

Notes

(a) A self-consistent set of values derived from absolute rate calculations.
(b) Review of literature data (refs. 3 to 6).
(c) Review of literature data (refs. 3 to 7).
(d) For a critical summary of the (then) available experimental data, see refs. 9 and 10.
(e) Recalculation of the data from ref. 11.
(f) Γ is the tunneling factor.

References

1. Polanyi, J. Chem. Phys. **23,** 1505 (1955).
2. Trotman-Dickenson, "Gas Kinetics," p. 169 et seq. (Butterworths, London, 1955).
3. Farkas and Farkas, Proc. Roy. Soc. **152A,** 124 (1935).
4. Geib and Harteck, Z. Phys. Chem. Bodenstein Festband 849 (1931).
5. Melville and Robb, Proc. Roy. Soc. **196A,** 445 (1949).
6. Van Meersche, Bull. Soc. Chim. Belg. **60,** 99 (1951).
7. Boata, Careri, Cimino, Molinari, and Volpi, J. Chem. Phys. **24,** 783 (1956).
8. Weston, J. Chem. Phys. **31,** 892 (1959).
9. Shavitt, J. Chem. Phys. **31,** 1359 (1959).
10. Rapp and Weston, J. Chem. Phys. **36,** 2807 (1962).
11. Schulz and Le Roy, J. Chem. Phys. **42,** 3869 (1965).
12. Ridley, Schulz, and Le Roy, J. Chem. Phys. **44,** 3344 (1966).
13. Schulz and Le Roy, Can. J. Chem. **42,** 2480 (1964).

Metathetical Reactions of Hydrogen Atoms

Reactants	Notes	E	$\log_{10} A$	Temperature range	Radical source	Reference
		(kcal mole^{-1})	*(cm^3 mole^{-1} sec^{-1})*	°C		
HYDROGEN ATOM TRANSFER						
Alkanes						
CH_4	(a)	7.0 ± 1.5		130–290		1
		6.6	10.5	99–163	H_2/tungsten filament	2
		4.5 ± 1.2	10.01 ± 0.2	99–163	H_2/tungsten filament	3

Reactants	Notes	E	$\log_{10} A$	Temperature range	Radical source	Reference
		(*kcal mole*$^{-1}$)	(*cm*^{3} *mole*$^{-1}$ *sec*$^{-1}$)	°C		
	(a)	9.0	12.5	130–420		4
	(a)	8.0	12.6	477–547		5
		11.5	14.3	950–1530	CH_4/O_2 flame	6
		15.1	14.53	400–480	H_2/O_2 ignition	7
	(b)	11.05	14.19			8
		$k=2.9\times10^{10}$		610	H_2/O_2 ignition	9
		7.4 ± 1.1	11.8	212–530	H_2/discharge	10
		8.0	13.9	697–863	H_2O_2 ignition	11
	(w) (q)	13.5		450	D_2/discharge	12
	(w) (c)	7.8	13.0	347–465	D_2CO photolysis	13
	(r)	9.6	12.6			
C_2H_2	(d)	1.5				14
C_2H_4	(e)	6.6 ± 1	13.26	500–625	H_2/O_2 ignition	15
C_2H_6		6.8	12.53	80–163	H_2/tungsten filament	16
		12.0	13.17	410–550	H_2O_2 ignition	17
	(e)	14 ± 1	14.76	500–625	H_2/O_2 ignition	15
	(q)	9.0 ± 0.2		24 ± 2	H_2/discharge	18
		12.2	14.52	410–550	H_2/O_2 ignition	7
	(f)	9.9 ± 1.0	14.20 ± 0.4	25–1230		19
		9.7 ± 2	14.1	720–1160	$C_2H_6/H_2/O_2$ flame	105
	(g)	$k=3.0\times10^{9}$		630		20
	(h)	9.0	13.5	50–250	C_2H_6/C_3H_6 radiolysis	21
	(f)	9.71 ± 0.58	14.12 ± 0.25	31–1227		22
		6.20	13.6	752–917	H_2/O_2 ignition	11
	(w) (i)	9.0	14.4	30–306	D_2S/C_2H_6 photolysis	23
C_3H_6	(e)	1.1 ± 1	12.45	500–625	H_2/O_2 ignition	15
	(w) (i)	5.0	13.7	25–205	$D_2S+C_3H_6$ photolysis	23
C_3H_8		8.5	13.43	410–550	H_2/O_2 ignition	17
	(e)	8.3 ± 1	13.56	500–625	H_2/O_2 ignition	15
		8.8	13.80	410–550	H_2/O_2 ignition	7
	(h)	7.4	13.7	57–217	C_3H_8 radiolysis	24
		8.2	14.12	95–170	H_2/tungsten filament	25
	(j)	$k=4.53\times10^{11}$		520	H_2/O_2 ignition	26
	(f)	7.83 ± 0.79	13.81 ± 0.37	28–520		26
	(w) (q)	8.0		Room temp.	H_2/discharge	27
	(w) (i)	7.2	14.5	30–250	$D_2S+C_3H_8$ photolysis	23
$CH_3CH{:}CHCH_3$	(w) (i)	5.0	14.1	28–230	$D_2S+C_4H_8$ photolysis	23
n-C_4H_{10}	(q)	8.9		Room temp.	H_2/discharge	27
	(j)	$k=5.1\times10^{11}$		520	H_2/O_2 ignition	28
	(f)	7.5 ± 0.5	13.9 ± 0.2	27–520		28
	(h)	6.7	13.3	50–250	$n-C_4H_{10}$ radiolysis	21
	(k)	7.1	13.82	70–170	H_2/tungsten filament	29
	(w) (q)	7.9		Room temp.	H_2/discharge	27
	(w) (i)	7.1	14.5	30–250	$D_2S+C_4H_{10}$ photolysis	23
i-C_4H_{10}	(q)	9.3			H_2/discharge	30
		6.0	13.47	410–550	H_2/O_2 ignition	17
	(e)	5.6 ± 1	12.89	500–625	H_2/O_2 ignition	15
		5.1	12.76	410–510	H_2/O_2 ignition	7
	(h)	5.1	13.1	50–250	i-C_4H_{10} radiolysis	21
	(j)	$k=9.2\times10^{11}$		520	H_2/O_2 ignition	28

Metathetical Reactions of Hydrogen Atoms – Continued

Reactants	Notes	E	$\log_{10} A$	Temperature range	Radical source	Reference
		(kcal mole⁻¹)	*(cm³ mole⁻¹ sec⁻¹)*	°C		
	(f)	6.8 ± 0.5	14.0 ± 0.2	27–520		28
	(w) (i)	6.3	14.5	30–350	$D_2S + C_4H_{10}$ photolysis	23
n-C_5H_{12}	(q)	8.5		Room temp.	H_2/discharge	27
	(w) (q)	7.8		Room temp.	D_2/discharge	27
neo-C_5H_{12}	(q)	9.2		Room temp.	H_2/discharge	31
n-C_6H_{14}	(q)	9.1		Room temp.	H_2/discharge	27
	(f)	5.9		25–305		32
	(w) (q)	8.0		Room temp.	D_2/discharge	27
Cyclo Alkanes						
cyclo-C_3H_6	(q)	9.5		Room temp.	H_2/discharge	27
	(w) (q)	9.3		Room temp.	D_2/discharge	27
cyclo-C_4H_8	(q)	8.2		Room temp.	H_2/discharge	27
	(w) (q)	7.7		Room temp.	D_2/discharge	27
cyclo-C_6H_{10}	(q)	7.5		Room temp.	H_2/discharge	27
	(w) (q)	6.6		Room temp.	D_2/discharge	27
cyclo-C_6H_{12}	(q)	8.0		Room temp.	H_2/discharge	27
	(w) (q)	7.2		Room temp.	D_2/discharge	27
Aromatic hydrocarbons						
C_6H_6	(q)	< 7		Room temp.	H_2/discharge	27
	(w) (q)	< 6		Room temp.	D_2/discharge	27
Aldehydes and ketones						
HCHO	(l)	2.6	13.21	252–397	H_2CO/D_2 photolysis	33
	(f)	3.49	13.46	327–727		34
	(f)	3.26	13.29	250–400		34
		$k = (2.7 \pm 0.7) \times 10^{10}$		27	H_2/discharge	35
		$k = 3.5 \times 10^{12}$		547	HCHO pyrolysis	36
	(w) (l)	2.7	13.21	252–397	H_2CO/D_2 photolysis	33
DCDO	(l)	3.6	13.21	252–397	H_2CO/D_2CO photolysis	33
	(w) (m)	3.0	13.3	308–341	D_2CO photolysis	13
	(w) (l)	3.6	13.21	252–397	H_2CO/D_2CO photolysis	33
CH_3CHO	(q)	≤ 6		25	H_2/discharge	37
CH_3COCH_3	(q)	8.8		Room temp.	H_2/discharge	38
	(w) (q)	8.0		Room temp.	D_2/discharge	38
Metal alkyl						
CH_3HgCH_3	(q)	≤ 6		25	H_2/ discharge	106
Halogenated methane						
CF_3H	(a)	5.0	12.7	832–1011	H_2/O_2 ignition	11

Metathetical Reactions of Hydrogen Atoms—Continued

Reactants	Notes	E	$\log_{10} A$	Temperature range	Radical source	Reference
		(kcal mole⁻¹)	*(cm³ mole⁻¹ sec⁻¹)*	°C		
Hydrogen halides						
H F	(n)	35.0	13.00	3527–5027	HF shock wave decomposition	39
H Cl		5.2	13.4	628–798	H_2/HCl thermal reaction	40
	(a)	4.5				41
H Br		2.2	13.79	832–1011	H_2/O_2 ignition	11
		0.9	13.1	548–711	H_2/HBr thermal reaction	42
	(o)	3.7	14.04	700–1400		43
	(r)	2.9	13.8			
HI		0.7 ± 0.25	13.70 ± 0.07	394–527	H_2/I_2 thermal reaction	44
		1.17 ± 0.35	13.8 ± 0.2	394–465	H_2/I_2 thermal reaction	107
Hydrides of oxygen and nitrogen						
H_2O		$k = 6.6 \pm 0.9 \times 10^9$		799	$H_2/O_2/N_2O$ flame	45
	(a)	20.4	13.96	37–642		108
	(a)	21.6	14.84	687–807	H_2/O_2 ignition	46
	(f)	21.1 ± 1.5	14.48 ± 1.0	27–1727		47
D_2O	(a)	25.5	15	1012–1227		109
			$k = 5.0 \times 10^9$	799	H_2/O_2 flame	48
			$k = 3.6 \times 10^9$	799	H_2/O_2 flame	49
	(p) (f)	21.8	13.93	799	H_2/O_2 flame	45
H_2O_2	(a)	18.8	16.39	687–807	H_2O_2 ignition	46
N_2H_4		2.0	11.54	25–150	H_2/ discharge	50

FLUORINE ATOM TRANSFER

Reactants	Notes	E	$\log_{10} A$	Temperature range	Radical source	Reference
SF_6		30 ± 5	15.3	1030–1670	H_2/O_2 and C_2H_2/O_2 flames	51

CHLORINE ATOM TRANSFER

Reactants	Notes	E	$\log_{10} A$	Temperature range	Radical source	Reference
HCl		0.9 ± 1.3		22–152	HCl/D_2 and DCl/H_2 photolysis	52
Cl_2		> 2.1		25–75	$H_2/Cl_2/O_2$ photolysis	53
		> 2.9				54
		> 1.8		25–100	$H_2/Cl_2/O_2$ photolysis	55
		> 1.6		0–85	$H_2/Cl_2/O_2$ photolysis	56
		< 2.5				57
CCl_4	(s)	~ 5		2034	Molecular beam	58

Metathetical Reactions of Hydrogen Atoms – Continued

Reactants	Notes	E	$\log_{10} A$	Temperature range	Radical source	Reference
		(*kcal mole*$^{-1}$)	(*cm*^{3} *mole*$^{-1}$ *sec*$^{-1}$)	°C		
BROMINE ATOM TRANSFER						
Br_2		3.7	14.97	700–1400		43
CF_3Br		17.45	15.64	832–1011	H_2/O_2 ignition	11
$C_2F_4Br_2$		14.5	16.0	855–1013	H_2/O_2 ignition	11
IODINE ATOM TRANSFER						
I_2		0.0 ± 0.5	14.6 ± 0.2	394–465	H_2/I_2 thermal reaction	107
OXYGEN ATOM TRANSFER						
O_2			$k = 5.0 \times 10^9$	485	H_2/O_2 ignition	60
			$k = 6.7 \times 10^9$	520	H_2/O_2 ignition	60
			$k = 2.7 \times 10^9$	520	H_2/O_2 ignition	61
			$k = 6.6 \times 10^8$	520	H_2/O_2 ignition	62
		15.1	13.75		H_2/O_2 ignition	63
			$k = 1.43 \times 10^{12}$	1380	H_2/O_2 ignition	64
		20.0 ± 2.0	14.9	1012–1227	H_2/O_2 flame	109
			$k = 1.5 \times 10^{11}$	827	H_2/O_2 flame	110
	(t)	14.9	13.72		H_2/O_2 ignition	65
		15.9 ± 0.8	13.89	570–660	$H_2/CO/O_2$ ignition	66
			$k = 6.0 \times 10^9$	540	H_2/O_2 ignition	34
		15.0 ± 0.6	13.59	590–660	$C_2H_6/CO/O_2$ ignition	111
		16.3		552–1089	H_2/O_2 ignition	67
		17.4 ± 0.7	14.82 ± 0.2	1853–2772	H_2/O_2 flame	68
	(a)		$k = 1.83 \times 10^3$	20		69
	(a)		$k = 3.28 \times 10^3$	37		70
	(f)	17.8 ± 1.0	15.08 ± 0.8	27–327		70
	(f)	16.9 ± 1.0	14.86 ± 0.8	1227–1427		70
		18.9 ± 0.9		620–1080	H_2/O_2 ignition	71
		15.6 ± 0.6	13.66	570–660	$H_2/CO/O_2$ ignition	72
	(f)	16.49 ± 0.70	14.31 ± 0.28	20–1377		73
		17.0	13.69	999–1923	C_2H_2/O_2 oxidation	74
		17.75	15.0	687–807	H_2/O_2 ignition	46
			$k = 1.6 \times 10^{10}$	642	H_2/O_2 flame	108
	(f)	16.50	14.34	20–1400		112
O_3			$k = (2.4 \pm 0.3) \times 10^{12}$	Room temp.	Diffusion flame	75
			$k = (1.6 \pm 0.3) \times 10^{12}$	Room temp.	H_2 discharge	76
H_2O_2	(u)		$k = (1.9 - 3.0) \times 10^{11}$	447	H_2O_2 ignition	77
	(u)		$k = 1.1 \times 10^{12}$	500	H_2/O_2 slow reaction	78
N_2O		16.3 ± 2.0	14.62	990–1510	$H_2/N_2O/O_2$ flame	110
			$k = 4.3 \times 10^{10}$	627	$H_2/N_2O/O_2$ flame	108
			$k = 2.9 \times 10^{11}$	1084	$H_2/N_2O/O_2$ flame	108
			$k = (4.3 \pm 1.5) \times 10^{10}$	627	$H_2/N_2O/O_2$ flame	45
	(f)	13 ± 1.5	13.7 ± 0.4	150–1487		45

Metathetical Reactions of Hydrogen Atoms—Continued

Reactants	Notes	E	$\log_{10} A$	Temperature range	Radical source	Reference
		($kcal\ mole^{-1}$)	($cm^3\ mole^{-1}\ sec^{-1}$)	°C		
NO_2		$k=3.2\times10^{13}$		227–267	H_2/Cl_2NO_2 thermal reaction	79
		$k=2.9\times10^{13}$		25	H_2/ discharge	80
		$k=(2.9\pm0.3)\times10^{13}$		Room temp.	H_2/ discharge	76
	(v)	$k=5.5\times10^{13}$		360	H_2/O_2 ignition	81
CO_2		33.3	15.48	944–1072	H_2/O_2 flame	113
	(b)	29.7	14.89	1000–1500		8
		$k=8.4\times10^{8}$		799	H_2/O_2 flame	49

Ratios of Rate Constants (Hydrogen Atoms)

(i) Reactions of the type (1) $H+RH=H_2+R$ where RH is any hydrogen containing compound.
(2) $H+OL=OLH$ where OL is an olefine.

RH	OL	Notes	k_1/k_2	E_1-E_2	$\log_{10} A_1/A_2$	Temperature range	Radical source	Reference
				($kcal\ mole^{-1}$)		°C		
CH_4	C_2H_4		2.6×10^{-6}			120	CH_4 -H	82
C_2H_4	C_2H_4		-1.0×10^{-3} (i.e. $=0$)			24	n-C_4H_{10} -H	83
C_2H_6	C_2H_4		2.5×10^{-5}			25	C_2H_6 radiolysis	84
C_3H_6	C_3H_6		4.5×10^{-2}			24	n-C_4H_{10} -H	83
			$(4.10\pm0.37)\times10^{-2}$			25	n-C_4H_{10} -H	85
C_3D_6	C_3D_6		$(6.3\pm2.3)\times10^{-2}$			25	n-C_4H_{10} -H	85
C_3H_8	C_2H_4		1.9×10^{-3}			25	C_3H_8 -H	86
			1.5×10^{-3}			24	C_3H_8 -H	87
C_3H_8	C_3H_6		5.2×10^{-4}			25	C_3H_8 radiolysis	88
1,3-C_4H_6	1,3-C_4H_6		3.2×10^{-2}			24	n-C_4H_{10} -H	83
1-C_4H_8	1-C_4H_8		8.1×10^{-2}			24	n-C_4H_{10} -H	83
i-C_4H_8	i-C_4H_8		2.0×10^{-2}			24	n-C_4H_{10} -H	83
cisC_4H_8-2	cisC_4H_8-2		6.6×10^{-2}			24	n-C_4H_{10} -H	83
transC_4H_8-2	transC_4H_8-2		11.7×10^{-2}			24	n-C_4H_{10} -H	83
n-C_4H_{10}	C_3H_6		1.4×10^{-3}			25	n-C_4H_{10} -H	85
n-C_4H_{10}	C_3D_6		1.3×10^{-3}			25	n-C_4H_{10} -H	85
i-C_4H_{10}	C_2H_4		8.6×10^{-3}			25	i-C_4H_{10} -H	86
			8.1×10^{-3}			24	i-C_4H_{10} -H	87

RH	OL	Notes	k_1/k_2	E_1-E_2	$\log_{10} A_1/A_2$	Temperature range	Radical source	Reference
				(kcal mole^{-1})		°C		
cyclo-C_5H_{10}	cyclo-C_5H_8		5.7×10^{-3}			24	cyclo-C_5H_{10} -H	89
n-C_5H_{12}	C_2H_4		3.7×10^{-3} 2.2×10^{-3}			25 24	n-C_5H_{12} -H n-C_5H_{12} -H	86 87
n-C_5H_{12}	C_5H_{10}	(y)	$\geqslant 4.5\times10^{-3}$			21	n-C_5H_{12} -H	114
i-C_5H_{12}	C_2H_4		10.6×10^{-3}			25	i-C_5H_{12} -H	86
$(CH_3)_2C$: $C(CH_3)_2$	$(CH_3)_2C$: $C(CH_3)_2$		-2.5×10^{-2} (i.e. = 0)			24	n-C_4H_{10} -H	83
n-C_6H_{14}	C_2H_4		3.7×10^{-3}			25	n-C_6H_{14} -H	86
neo-C_6H_{14}	C_2H_4		1.8×10^{-3}			25	neo-C_6H_{14} -H	86
$(CH_3)_2CHCH_2$ CH_2CH_3	C_2H_4		11.6×10^{-3}			25	$(CH_3)_2CHCH_2CH_2$ -H CH_3 -H	86
$(CH_3)_2CHCH$ $(CH_3)_2$	C_2H_4		21.0×10^{-3}			25	$(CH_3)_2CHCH$ $(CH_3)_2$ -H	86
H_2S	C_2H_4		0.5			30	H_2S photolysis	90
CH_3SH	C_2H_4			0.54 ± 0.12	0.59	50–220	CH_3SH photolysis	91

(ii) Miscellaneous reactions of hydrogen atoms with hydrocarbons and hydrocarbon derivatives.

Reaction	Notes	E_1-E_2	$\log_{10}A_1/A_2$	k_1/k_2	Temperature range	Radical source	Reference
		(kcal mole^{-1})			°C		
(1) $H+CCl_3D=CCl_3+HD$ (2) $H+CCl_3D=CCl_2D+HCl$				1.1	Room temp.	H_2/ discharge	92
(1) $H+CCl_3Br=CCl_3+HBr$ (2) $H+CCl_3Br=CCl_2Br+HCl$				0.49	Room temp.	H_2/ discharge	115
(1) $H+CCl_3F=CCl_3+HF$ (2) $H+CCl_3F=CCl_2F+HCl$				0.071	Room temp.	H_2/ discharge	115
(1) $H+CCl_2BrH=CCl_2Br+H_2$ (2) $H+CCl_2BrH$ $=CClBrH+HCl$				1.7	Room temp.	H_2/ discharge	92
(1) $H+CCl_2BrH$ $=CCl_2H+HBr$ (2) $H+CCl_2BrH$ $=CClBrH+HCl$				0.8	Room temp.	H_2/ discharge	92
(1) $H+C_3H_6=C_3H_5+H_2$ (2) $H+C_3H_8=C_3H_7+H_2$				32	25	C_3H_8 radiolysis	88
(1) $H+(CH_3)_3CD=C_4H_9+HD$ (2) $H+(CH_3)_3CD$ $=C_4H_8D+H_2$				1.2	25	i-C_4H_9D photolysis	93

247-168 O-67—2

Ratios of Rate Constants (Hydrogen Atoms) – Continued

Reaction	Notes	E_1-E_2	$\log_{10}A_1/A_2$	k_1/k_2	Temperature range	Radical source	Reference
		(*kcal mole*$^{-1}$)			°C		
(1) $D+(CH_3)_3CD=C_4H_9+D_2$ (2) $D+(CH_3)_3CD$ $=C_4H_8D+HD$				1.2	25	i-C_4H_9D photolysis	93
(1) $H+i$-C_5H_{12} $=C_5H_{11}+H_2$ (2) $H+C_5H_{11}=C_5H_{10}+H_2$	(z)			5.2×10^{-2}	25	i-C_5H_{12}-H	94
(1) $H+1$-$C_5H_{10}=C_5H_9+H_2$ (2) $H+n$-$C_5H_{12}=C_5H_{11}+H_2$				8.8	21	n-C_5H_{12}-H	88
(1) $H+i$-$C_5H_{12}=C_5H_{11}+H_2$ (2) $H+C_5H_{11}=C_5H_{12}$	(z)			5.9×10^{-3}	25	i-C_5H_{12}-H	94
(1) $H+n$-$C_6H_{14}=C_6H_{13}+H_2$ (2) $H+C_6H_{13}=C_6H_{14}$				5.3×10^{-3} 1.3×10^{-3}	25 25	n-C_6H_{14}-H n-C_6H_{14}/1-C_6H_{12}-H	94 94
(1) $H+CH_3CH{:}CHCHO$ $=CH_3CH{:}CHCO+H_2$ (2) $H+CH_3CH{:}CHCHO$ $=CH_3CH{:}CH_2+HCO$		~ 0.5			210–350	$(CH_3)_2CO$/ $CH_3CH{:}CHCHO$ photolysis	95

(iii) Reactions of the type (1) $H+HX=H_2+X$
(2) $H+X_2=HX+X$ where X is a halogen

Reaction	Notes	E_1-E_2	$\log_{10}A_1/A_2$	k_1/k_2	Temperature range	Radical source	Reference
(1) $H+HCl=H_2+Cl$ (2) $H+Cl_2=HCl+Cl$		1.54 ± 0.13	-0.84 ± 0.1	$\leqslant0.05$	25 0–62	H_2/Cl_2 photolysis H_2/Cl_2 photolysis	96 97
(1) $H+HBr=H_2+Br$ (2) $H+Br_2=HBr+Br$	(aa)			0.12 0.1 0.12 ± 0.009 0.099 ±0.007	327–1197 162–310 25–300 1027–1427	H_2/Br_2 thermal reaction H_2/Br_2 photolysis H_2/Br_2 thermal reaction H_2/Br_2 thermal reaction	98 99 100 101
(1) $H+HI=H_2+I$ (2) $H+I_2=HI+I$				0.070 ± 0.02 0.082 ±0.012 0.06	394 527 700	H_2/I_2 thermal reaction H_2/I_2 thermal reaction	44 44 102
(1) $D+DI=D_2+I$ (2) $D+I_2=DI+I$				0.073	527	D_2/I_2 thermal reaction	116

(iv) Miscellaneous Ratios

Reaction	Notes	E_1-E_2	$\log_{10}A_1/A_2$	k_1/k_2	Temperature range	Radical source	Reference
(1) $H+D_2=HD+D$ (2) $H+HCl=H_2+Cl$				14 ± 4	22	HCl/D_2 photolysis	52
(1) $D+HD=D_2+H$ (2) $D+DCl=D_2+Cl$				65	22	H_2/DCl photolysis	52
(1) $D+HCl=HD+Cl$ (2) $D+HCl=DCl+H$				0.5 ± 0.4 $5.\pm4$	22 152	D_2/HCl photolysis	52 52

Ratios of Rate Constants (Hydrogen Atoms) – Continued

Reaction	Notes	E_1-E_2	$\log_{10}A_1/A_2$	k_1/k_2	Temperature range	Radical source	Reference
		(*kcal mole*$^{-1}$)			°C		
(1) $H+D_2=HD+D$ (2) $H+HBr=H_2+Br$				0.55	22	D_2/HBr photolysis	52
(1) $H+NO_2=NO+OH$ (2) $H+Cl_2=HCl+Cl$		−3.13	0.42		227–267	$H_2/Cl_2/NO_2$ thermal reaction	79
(1) $D+C_2H_6=C_2H_5+HD$ (2) $D+DI=D_2+I$				1.2×10^{-3} 8.7×10^{-3}	25 100	DI photolysis DI photolysis	103 103
(1) $H+H_2S=HS+H_2$ (2) $H+O_2=HO_2$				0.60 0.137 0.171	50 93 100	H_2S photo-oxidation	104

Notes

(a) Estimated from the reverse reaction.

(b) This value was used by the authors in the region 1000–1500 °C, but its origin was not stated.

(c) Measured relative to $D+D_2CO=D_2+DCO$ for which $k=10^{13.30}$ exp (−3000 *RT*).

(d) Private communication from Asaba.

(e) Taken from Tikhomirova and Voevodsky, "Chain oxidation of Hydrocarbons in the Gas Phase" (Russ), Moscow, 1955.

(f) Critical survey of literature data.

(g) "A rough estimate."

(h) Measured relative to $H+C_3H_6=C_3H_7$ for which $k=10^{13.5}$ exp (−2600/RT).

(i) Measured relative to $D+H_2=HD+H$ for which $k=10^{13.4}$ exp (−5000/RT).

(j) Measured relative to $H+O_2=OH+O$ for which $k=5.1\times10^{9}$ at 520 °C.

(k) Measured relative to $H+C_3H_8=C_3H_7+H_2$ for which $k=10^{14.11}$ exp (−8200/RT).

(l) Measured relative to $D+H_2=HD+H$ for which $k=10^{13.92}$ exp (−6000/RT).

(m) Measured relative to $D+H_2=HD+H$ for which $k=10^{13.46}$ exp (−5400/RT).

(n) Rate constant estimated in computer calculations. E value assumed and A factor varied.

(o) Estimated from kinetic data.

(p) The value of E was assumed, and A calculated from the rate constant.

(q) A steric factor of 0.1 was assumed.

(r) Calculated from the recommended value for the reverse reaction.

(s) Steric factor = 0.13.

(t) Used at flame temperatures.

(u) Measured relative to $H+O_2=OH+O$ for which $k=10^{14.31}$ exp (−16500/RT).

(v) Measured relative to $H+O_2+H_2=HO_2+H_2$ for which $k=5.5\times10^{15}$ cm^6 mole^2 sec^{-1}

(w) Reactions with D atoms.

(x) Calculated from the recommended value for the reverse reaction.

(y) C_5H_{10} refers to the mixture of pentenes formed in the primary reaction.

(z) C_5H_{11} is a radical formed in the primary process, probably either $CH_3C(CH_3)CH_2CH_3$ or $CH_3CH(CH_3)CHCH_3$.

(aa) The author shows that this value is compatible with his results in the temperature range shown.

References

1. Majury and Steacie, Disc. Faraday Soc. **14,** 45 (1953).
2. Le Roy, Disc. Faraday Soc. **14,** 120 (1953).
3. Berlie and Le Roy, Can. J. Chem. **32,** 650 (1954).
4. Pritchard, Pyke, and Trotman-Dickenson, J. Am. Chem. Soc. **77,** 2629 (1955).
5. Benson and Jain, J. Chem. Phys. **31,** 1008 (1959).
6. Fenimore and Jones, J. Phys. Chem. **65,** 2200 (1961).
7. Gorban and Nalbandyan, Russ. J. Phys. Chem. **36,** 946 (1962).
8. Intezarova, Kondratiev, and Mukhoyan, Kinetika i Kataliz **5,** 585 (1964).
9. Azatyan, Nalbandyan, and Tsui, Kinetika i Kataliz **5,** 201 (1964).
10. Jamieson and Brown, Can. J. Chem. **42,** 1638 (1964).
11. Skinner and Ringrose, J. Chem. Phys. **43,** 4129 (1965).
12. Steacie, Can. J. Res. **15B,** 264 (1937).
13. Klein, McNesby, Scheer, and Schoen, J. Chem. Phys. **30,** 58 (1959).
14. Chase and Weinberg, Proc. Roy. Soc. **275A,** 411 (1963).
15. Voevodsky and Kondratiev, "Progress in Reaction Kinetics," p. 41 (Pergamon Press, 1961).
16. Berlie and Le Roy, Disc. Faraday Soc. **14,** 50 (1953).
17. Gorban and Nalbandyan, Dokl. Akad. Nauk. S.S.S.R. **132,** 1335 (1960).
18. Trost and Steacie, J. Chem. Phys. **16,** 361 (1948).
19. Baldwin, 9th Int. Comb. Symp., p. 604 (Academic Press, N.Y., 1963).
20. Blackmore and Hinshelwood, Proc. Roy. Soc. **271A,** 34 (1963).
21. Yang, J. Phys. Chem. **67,** 562 (1963).
22. Baldwin and Melvin, J. Chem. Soc. 1785 (1964).
23. Darwent and Roberts, Disc. Faraday Soc. **14,** 55 (1953).
24. Yang, J. Am. Chem. Soc. **84,** 3795 (1962).
25. Kazmi, Diefendorf, and Le Roy, Can. J. Chem. **41,** 690 (1963).
26. Baldwin, Trans. Faraday Soc. **60,** 527 (1964).
27. Schiff and Steacie, Can. J. Chem. **29,** 1 (1951).
28. Baldwin and Walker, Trans. Faraday Soc. **60,** 1236 (1964).
29. Kazmi and Le Roy, Can. J. Chem. **42,** 1145 (1964).

30. White, Winkler, and Kenalty, Can. J. Res. **20B,** 255 (1942).
31. Trost and Steacie, J. Chem. Phys. **16,** 361 (1948).
32. Norrish and Purnell, Proc. Roy. Soc. **243A,** 449 (1958).
33. McNesby, Scheer, and Klein, J. Chem. Phys. **32,** 1814 (1960).
34. Baldwin and Cowe, Trans. Faraday Soc. **58,** 1768 (1962).
35. Brennen, Gay, Glass, and Niki, J. Chem. Phys. **43,** 2569 (1965).
36. Klein, Scheer, and Schoen, J. Am. Chem. Soc. **78,** 50 (1956).
37. Trost, Darwent, and Steacie, J. Chem. Phys. **16,** 353 (1948).
38. Harris and Steacie, J. Chem. Phys. **13,** 554 (1945).
39. Jacobs, Giedt, and Cohen, J. Chem. Phys. **43,** 3688 (1965).
40. Steiner and Rideal, Proc. Roy. Soc. **173A,** 503 (1939).
41. Bigeleisen, Klein, Weston, and Wolfsberg, J. Chem. Phys. **30,** 1340 (1959).
42. Steiner Proc. Roy. Soc. **173A,** 531 (1939).
43. Cooley and Anderson, Ind. and Eng. Chem. **44,** 1402 (1952).
44. Sullivan, J. Chem. Phys. **36,** 1925 (1962).
45. Dixon-Lewis, Sutton, and Williams, J. Chem. Soc. 5724 (1965).
46. Skinner and Ringrose, J. Chem. Phys. **42,** 2190 (1965).
47. Kaufman and Del Greco, 9th Int. Comb. Symp., p. 659 (Academic Press, N.Y., 1963).
48. Dixon-Lewis, Sutton, and Williams, Disc. Faraday Soc. **33,** 205 (1962).
49. Dixon-Lewis, Sutton, and Williams, Trans. Faraday Soc. **61,** 255 (1965).
50. Schiavello and Volpi, J. Chem. Phys. **37,** 1510 (1962).
51. Fenimore and Jones, Comb. and Flame **8,** 231 (1964).
52. DeVries and Klein, J. Chem. Phys. **41,** 3428 (1964).
53. Hertel, Z. Phys. Chem. **15B,** 325 (1931).
54. Padoa and Butirone, Accad. Lincei, **25,** 215 (1916); and Gazz. Chim. Ital. **47,** 6 (1917).
55. Porter, Bardwell, and Lind, J. Am. Chem. Soc. **48,** 2603 (1926).
56. Krauskopf and Rollefson, J. Am. Chem. Soc. **56,** 327 (1934).
57. Trotman-Dickenson, "Gas Kinetics," p. 184 (Butterworths, London, 1955).
58. Seidel, Martin, and Mietzner, Z. Phys. Chem. **47B,** 348 (1965).
59. Campbell and Hirschfelder, Univ. of Wisconsin report CF–2108 NORD 9938.
60. Semenoff, Acta. Physicochim. **20,** 291 (1945).
61. Baldwin, Trans. Faraday Soc. **52,** 1344 (1956).
62. Baldwin and Simmons, Trans. Faraday Soc. **53,** 964 (1957).
63. Semenoff, Nalbandyan, and Karmilova, Zhur. Phys. Chem. **32,** 1193 (1957).
64. Schott and Kinsey, J. Chem. Phys. **29,** 1177 (1958).
65. Kondratiev, 7th Int. Comb. Symp., p. 41 (Butterworths, London, 1959).
66. Azatyan, Voevodskii, and Nalbandyan, Kinetika i Kataliz **2,** 340 (1961).
67. Fujimoto, Bull. Chem. Soc. Japan **36,** 1233 (1963).
68. Lovachev, Comb. and Flame **7,** 388 (1963).
69. Clyne, 9th Int. Comb. Symp., p. 211 (Academic Press, N.Y., 1963).
70. Kaufman and Del Greco, 9th Int. Comb. Symp., p. 659 (Academic Press, N.Y., 1963).
71. Miyama and Takeyama, J. Chem. Phys. **41,** 2287 (1964).
72. Azatyan, Nalbandyan, and Tsui, Kinetika i Kataliz **5,** 201 (1964).
73. Baldwin and Melvin, J. Chem. Soc. 1785 (1964).
74. Glass, Kistiakowsky, Michael, and Niki, J. Chem. Phys. **42,** 608 (1965).
75. Garvin and McKinley, J. Chem. Phys. **24,** 1256 (1956).
76. Phillips and Schiff, J. Chem. Phys. **37,** 1233 (1962).
77. Forst and Giguere, J. Phys. Chem. **62,** 340 (1958).
78. Baldwin and Mayor, Trans. Faraday Soc. **56,** 103 (1960).
79. Rosser and Wise, J. Phys. Chem. **65,** 532 (1961).
80. Schiff, Disc. Faraday Soc. **33,** 285 (1962).
81. Ashmore and Tyler, Trans. Faraday Soc. **58,** 1108 (1962).
82. Back and Van der Auwera, Can. J. Chem. **40,** 2339 (1962).
83. Jennings and Cvetanovic, J. Chem. Phys. **35,** 1233 (1961).
84. Yang and Gant, J. Phys. Chem. **65,** 1861 (1961).
85. Takahasi and Cvetanovic, Can. J. Chem. **40,** 1037 (1962).
86. Holroyd and Klein, J. Phys. Chem. **67,** 2273 (1963).
87. Holroyd and Pierce, J. Phys. Chem. **68,** 1392 (1964).
88. Back, J. Phys. Chem. **64,** 124 (1960).
89. Stock and Gunning, Can. J. Chem. **38,** 2295 (1960).
90. Arthur and Bell, J. Chem. Soc. 4866 (1962).
91. Inaba and Darwent, J. Phys. Chem. **64,** 1431 (1960).
92. Clark and Tedder, Trans. Faraday Soc. **62,** 405 (1966).
93. Okabe and Becker, J. Am. Chem. Soc. **84,** 4004 (1962).
94. Kuntz, J. Phys. Chem. **69,** 2291 (1965).
95. Pitts, Thompson, and Woolfolk, J. Am. Chem. Soc. **80,** 66 (1958).
96. Bigeleisen, Klein, Weston, and Wolfsberg, J. Chem. Phys. **30,** 1340 (1959).
97. Klein and Wolfsberg, J. Chem. Phys. **34,** 1494 (1961).
98. Levy, J. Phys. Chem. **62,** 570 (1958).
99. Bodenstein and Lutkemeyer, Z. Phys. Chem. **114,** 208 (1924).
100. Bodenstein and Jung, Z. Phys. Chem. **121,** 127 (1926).
101. Britton and Cole, J. Phys. Chem. **65,** 1302 (1961).
102. Horie, Ishii, and Amano, J. Phys. Chem. **68,** 1264 (1964).
103. Carter, Hamill, and Williams, J. Am. Chem. Soc. **77,** 6457 (1955).
104. Darwent and Krasnansky, 7th Int. Comb. Symp., p. 3 (Butterworths, London, 1959).
105. Fenimore and Jones, 9th Int. Comb. Symp., p. 597 (Academic Press, N.Y., 1963).
106. Harris and Steacie, J. Chem. Phys. **13,** 559 (1945).
107. Sullivan, J. Chem. Phys. **30,** 1292 (1959).
108. Dixon-Lewis, Sutton, and Williams, 10th Int. Comb. Symp., p. 495 (Comb. Inst. Pittsburgh, 1965).
109. Fenimore and Jones, J. Phys. Chem. **62,** 693 (1958).
110. Fenimore and Jones, J. Phys. Chem. **63,** 1154 (1959).
111. Azatyan, Nalbandyan, and Tsui, Dokl. Akad. Nauk. S.S.S.R. **147,** 361 (1962).
112. Westenberg and Fristrom, 10th Int. Comb. Symp., p. 473 (Comb. Inst. Pittsburgh, 1965).
113. Fenimore and Jones, J. Phys. Chem. **62,** 1578 (1958).
114. Back, Trans. Faraday Soc. **54,** 512 (1958).
115. Clark and Tedder, Trans. Faraday Soc. **62,** 399 (1966).
116. Sullivan, J. Chem. Phys. **39,** 3001 (1963).

Review

1. Thrush, "Progress in Reaction Kinetics," Vol. 3, p. 65 (Pergamon Press, London, 1965).

Metathetical Reactions of Fluorine Atoms

Reactants	Notes	E	$\log_{10} A$	Temperature range	Radical source		Reference
			HYDROGEN ATOM TRANSFER				
Hydrogen		*(kcal mole^{-1})*	*(cm^3 mole^{-1} sec^{-1})*	°C			
H_2	(a)	1.71 ± 0.22	14.07	25–150	$CH_4/H_2/F_2$	P	1, 4
Alkanes							
CH_4	(a)	1.21 ± 0.80	14.09	−75–78	$CH_4/C_2H_6/F_2$	T	2, 4
C_2H_6		0.28	13.78	−60–20	standard	T	2, 4
$\mathbf{CH_3}CH_2\mathbf{CH_3}$	(a)	0.00 ± 0.25	13.52	−60–20	$C_2H_6/C_3H_8/F_2$	T	2, 4
$CH_3\mathbf{CH_2}CH_3$	(a)	0.00 ± 0.25	13.10	−60–20	$C_2H_6/C_3H_8/F_2$	T	2, 4
$\mathbf{CH_3}CH_2CH_2\mathbf{CH_3}$	(a)	0.00 ± 0.70	13.46	−60–20	n-$C_4H_{10}/C_3H_8/F_2$	T	2, 3, 4
$CH_3\mathbf{CH_2}\mathbf{CH_2}CH_3$	(a)	0.00 ± 0.65	13.37	−60–20	n-$C_4H_{10}/C_3H_8/F_2$	T	2, 3, 4
$(\mathbf{CH_3})_3CH$	(a)	0.00 ± 0.70	13.65	−60–20	n-C_4H_{10}/i-C_4H_{10}/F_2	T	2, 3, 4
$(CH_3)_3\mathbf{CH}$	(a)	0.00 ± 0.80	12.84	−60–20	n-C_4H_{10}/i-C_4H_{10}/F_2	T	2, 3, 4
$(CH_3)_4C$	(a)	0.00 ± 0.80	13.75	−60–20	i-$C_4H_{10}/(CH_3)_4C/F_2$	T	2, 4
Cyclo-Alkane							
cyclo-C_3H_6	(a)	0.00 ± 0.10	13.46		cyclo-$C_3H_6/C_3H_8/F_2$	T	2, 4
			CHLORINE ATOM TRANSFER				
CCl_4		$k = 2\times10^{13}$		20	CCl_4/F_2	T	5
			OXYGEN ATOM TRANSFER				
O_3		2.8		0–20	F_2/O_3	P	6

Notes

(a) These values are based on the assumed value $k = 10^{13.78}\exp(-280/RT)$ for the reaction $F + C_2H_6 = C_2H_5 + HF$.

References

1. Mercer and Pritchard, J. Phys. Chem. **63,** 1468 (1959).
2. Fettis, Knox, and Trotman-Dickenson, J. Chem. Soc. 1064 (1960).
3. Anson, Fredricks, and Tedder, J. Chem. Soc. 918 (1959).
4. Fettis and Knox, "Progress in Reaction Kinetics," Vol. 2, p. 3 (Pergamon Press, N.Y., 1964).
5. Clark and Tedder, J. Phys. Chem. **68,** 2018 (1964).
6. Starico, Sicre, and Schumacher, Anales Assoc. Quim. Argentina **50,** 120 (1962).

Reviews

1. Fettis and Knox, "Progress in Reaction Kinetics," Vol. 2, p. 3 (Pergamon Press, N.Y., 1964).
2. Fettis, Knox, and Trotman-Dickenson, Can. J. Chem. **38,** 1643 (1960).

Reaction of Chlorine Atoms

Index

Metathetical Reactions of Chlorine Atoms

Reactants	Notes	E	$\log_{10} A$	Temperature range	Radical source		References
		HYDROGEN ATOM TRANSFER					
		(*kcal mole*$^{-1}$)	(*cm*^{3} *mole*$^{-1}$ *sec*$^{-1}$)	°C			
Hydrogen							
H_2		$\geqslant 5.9$		25–75	H_2/Cl_2	P	1
		$\geqslant 5.8$		−73–23	H_2/Cl_2	P	2
		6.1 ± 1.0	14.3	0–25	Cl_2 discharge		3, 38
		$k = (4.8 \pm 0.4) \times 10^{11}$		250	$H_2/Cl_2/NO$	T	5, 6
		5.9		628–798	H_2/HCl	T	4
	(a)	5.48 ± 0.14	13.92 ± 0.03	0–798			7, 5
		5.48	13.92				
HD	(b)	5.97	13.83	−33–77	$H_2/HD/Cl_2$	P	8, 41
HT	(b)	6.03	13.79	−38–72	$H_2/HT/Cl_2$	P	9
	(b)	6.28	13.82	−30–70	$H_2/HD/HT/Cl_2$	P	41
D_2	(b)	6.60	13.78	0–32	$H_2/CO/Cl_2$	P	10, 11, 7
	(b)	6.70	13.84	30–178	$H_2/D_2/Cl_2$	P	12
	(b)	6.61	13.76	−30–70	$HD/D_2/Cl_2$	P	41
DT	(b)	6.90	13.73	−30–70	$DT/D_2/Cl_2$	P	41
T_2	(b)	7.17	13.73	−30–70	$T_2/D_2/Cl_2$	P	41
Alkanes							
CH_4	(b)	3.85 ± 0.18	13.42	20–211	$CH_4/H_2/Cl_2$	P	13, 16
CD_4	(i)	5.76	13.73	31–188	$CH_4/CD_4/Cl_2$	P	12
C_2H_6	(b)	1.04 ± 0.08	13.96	−41–385	$CH_4/C_2H_6/Cl_2$	P	14, 15
	(b)	1.00	14.08	76–290	$CH_4/C_2H_6/Cl_2$	P	16
C_2D_6	(i)	1.32	13.75	30–160	$C_2H_6/C_2D_6/Cl_2$	P	12
C_3H_8	(b)	0.67	14.28	25–211	$C_3H_8/C_2H_6/Cl_2$	P	16
$C\mathbf{H}_3CH_2C\mathbf{H}_3$	(b)	0.98	14.03	−70–230	$C_2H_6/C_3H_8/Cl_2$	P	14, 15
$CH_3C\mathbf{H}_2CH_3$	(b)	0.66	13.87	−70–230	$C_2H_6/C_3H_8/Cl_2$	P	14, 15
$C\mathbf{H}_3CH_2CH_2C\mathbf{H}_3$	(b)	0.77	13.93	−70–200	C_2H_6/n-C_4H_{10}/Cl_2	P	14, 17
$CH_3C\mathbf{H}_2C\mathbf{H}_2CH_3$	(b)	0.25	13.95	−70–200	C_2H_6/n-C_4H_{10}/Cl_2	P	14, 17
$(CH_3)_3CH$	(b)	0.86	14.29	25–211	C_2H_6/i-C_4H_{10}/Cl_2	P	16
$(C\mathbf{H}_3)_3CH$	(b)	0.80	14.09	−80–100	C_2H_6/i-C_4H_{10}/Cl_2	P	14, 17
$(CH_3)_3C\mathbf{H}$	(b)	0.02	13.24	−80–100	C_2H_6/i-C_4H_{10}/Cl_2	P	14, 17
$(CH_3)_4C$	(b)	0.90	14.25	−70–230	$C_3H_8/(CH_3)_4C/Cl_2$	P	14
	(b)	0.70	14.09	25–211	$C_2H_6/(CH_3)_4C/Cl_2$	P	16
Cyclo-alkanes							
cyclo-C_3H_6	(b)	4.12	13.73	20–260	C_2H_6/cyclo-C_3H_6/Cl_2	P	14

Metathetical Reactions of Chlorine Atoms—Continued

Reactants	Notes	E	$\log_{10} A$	Temperature range	Radical source		References
		(*kcal mole*$^{-1}$)	(*cm*^{3} *mole*$^{-1}$ *sec*$^{-1}$)	°C			
cyclo-C_4H_8	(b)	0.80	14.43	−30–105	C_3H_8/cyclo-C_4H_8/Cl_2	P	14
cyclo-C_5H_{10}	(b)	0.58	14.47	25–211	C_2H_6/cyclo-C_5H_{10}/Cl_2	P	16
Halogenated alkanes							
CH_3Cl	(b)	3.36	13.76	25–211	$CH_4/CH_3Cl/Cl_2$	P	16
	(b)	3.3 ± 0.1	13.5 ± 0.7	0–300	CH_3Cl/various RH/Cl_2 P	P	18
	(c)	3.08	13.5	85–180	$C_2Cl_4/CH_3Cl/Cl_2$	P	19
CH_2Cl_2		5.5	14.6				28
		3.0	13.43	0–300	CH_2Cl_2/various RH/Cl_2 P	P	18
	(c)	3.12	13.4	110–210	$C_2Cl_4/CH_2Cl_2/Cl_2$	P	19
$CHCl_3$		6.5	14.6				28
		3.35	12.84	0–300	$CH_4/CHCl_3/Cl_2$	P	18, 27
	(c)	3.33	13.2	140–210	$C_2Cl_4/CHCl_3/Cl_2$	P	19, 20, 21
$CDCl_3$	(d)	4.06 ± 0.2	12.69	−20–180	$CHCl_3/CDCl_3/Cl_2$	P	22
	(d)	4.79	13.30	109–203	$CHCl_3/CDCl_3/Cl_2$	P	12
C_2H_5Cl	(b)	1.50 ± 0.2	13.66	25–211	$C_2H_6/C_2H_5Cl/Cl_2$	P	16
CH_2ClCH_2Cl		3.0	13.4				23
$C_2H_3Cl_3$		3.5	13.5				23
$CHCl_2CHCl_2$		3.3	13.8				23
C_2HCl_5		5.4	13.9				28
		3.3	12.8	110–210	$C_2Cl_4/C_2HCl_5/Cl_2$	P	19, 24
		3.4	12.7				18
$CH_3CH_2CH_2C\mathbf{H}_2F$	(e)	0.77 ± 0.10	13.0	0–230	C_4H_9F/Cl_2	P	25, 26, 29
$CH_3CH_2C\mathbf{H}_2CH_2F$	(e)	0.62 ± 0.15	13.1	0–230	C_4H_9F/Cl_2	P	25, 26, 29
$CH_3C\mathbf{H}_2CH_2CH_2F$	(e)	(0.37 ± 0.10)	(13.3)	0–230	C_4H_9F/Cl_2	P	25, 26, 29
$C\mathbf{H}_3CH_2CH_2CH_2F$	(e)	0.77	13.1	0–230	C_4H_9F/Cl_2	P	25, 26, 29
$CH_3CH_2CH_2C\mathbf{H}_2Cl$	(e)	0.77 ± 0.20	13.4	35–146	C_4H_9Cl/Cl_2	P	26, 29
$CH_3CH_2C\mathbf{H}_2CH_2Cl$	(e)	0.30 ± 0.40	13.3	35–146	C_4H_9Cl/Cl_2	P	26, 29
$\mathbf{CH_3CH_2CH_2CH_2Cl}$	(e)	0.22 ± 0.10	13.7	35–146	C_4H_9Cl/Cl_2	P	26, 29
$C\mathbf{H}_3CH_2CH_2CH_2Cl$	(e)	(0.77)	(13.4)	35–146	C_4H_9Cl/Cl_2	P	26, 29
$CF_3C\mathbf{H}_2CH_2CH_2CH_3$	(e)	2.0	12.2	0–230	$CF_3C_4H_9/Cl_2$	P	25
$CF_3CH_2C\mathbf{H}_2CH_2CH_3$	(e)	0.6	13.0	0–230	$CF_3C_4H_9/Cl_2$	P	25

Metathetical Reactions of Chlorine Atoms—Continued

Reactants	Notes	E	$\log_{10} A$	Temperature range	Radical source	References
		(kcal mole⁻¹)	*(cm³ mole⁻¹ sec⁻¹)*	°C		
$CF_3CH_2CH_2C\mathbf{H}_2CH_3$	(e)	(0.3)	(13.3)	0–230	$CF_3C_4H_9/Cl_2$ P	25
$CF_3CH_2CH_2CH_2C\mathbf{H}_3$	(e)	0.5	12.8	0–230	$CF_3C_4H_9/Cl_2$ P	25
Hydrogen Halide						
HCl		6.57 ± 0.49		39–150	$HCL/D_2/Cl_2$ P	39
CHLORINE ATOM TRANSFER						
Halogenated alkanes						
CH_3Cl	(f) (g)	25.0	14.0			23, 30
CH_2Cl_2	(f) (g)	21.4	14.0			23, 30
$CHCl_3$	(f) (g)	21.0	14.0			23, 30
CCl_4	(f)	18.9	14.3			23
	(h)	20.0	14.0			28
C_2H_5Cl	(f)	21.5	14.3			23, 30
CH_2ClCH_2Cl	(f)	21.3	14.3			23, 30
$CHCl_2CH_2Cl$	(f)	20.6	14.3			23, 30
$CHCl_2CHCl_2$	(f)	20.4	14.3			23, 30
$CHCl_2CCl_3$	(h)	19.0	14.5			28
	(f)	18.3	14.3			23, 30
	(f)	17.9 ± 1.0	13.8 ± 0.5			31
C_2Cl_6	(f)	19.5	14.4			23
	(h)	18.0	13.5			28
Halogens and pseudo-halogens						
BrCl	(h)	1.1 ± 0.4	12.3	20–60		32
ICl		4.5	11.7	30–60	ICl P	33, 35
CNCl		34	14	1727–2527	ClCN S.T.	34
Carbonyls, etc.						
COCl		0.83	14.6	25–55	CO/Cl_2 P	36
$COCl_2$	(h)	19.9	14.4	25–55		28
	(a)	23.5	14.5	15–450		43

Reactants	Notes	E	$\log_{10} A$	Temperature range	Radical source		References
		(*kcal mole*$^{-1}$)	(*cm*^{3} *mole*$^{-1}$ *sec*$^{-1}$)	°C			
NOCl		1.06	13.06	25–55	$CO/NOCl/Cl_2$	P	35
Cl_2O		$k > 4 \times 10^{11}$			Cl_2O	F.P.	40
BROMINE ATOM TRANSFER							
Br_2		$k = (2.3 \pm 0.6) \times 10^{11}$		20	Br_2/Cl_2	P	32
OXYGEN ATOM TRANSFER							
N_2O		33.5	14.11	654–758	N_2O/Cl_2	T	37
MISCELLANEOUS REACTIONS							
$Cl + Na_2 = NaCl + Na$		$k = 1.5 \times 10^{14}$		~ 300	Na/Cl_2	D.F.	42

Notes

(a) Critical survey of literature data.

(b) Estimated assuming $k = 10^{13.92} \exp(-5480/RT)$ for the reaction $H_2 + Cl = HCl + H$.

(c) Activation energies are plotted to be in agreement with values found by Knox (ref. 18). The *A* factors are then adjusted to give the most consistent set of values for the rate constants.

(d) Calculated assuming $k = 10^{12.84} \exp(-3350/RT)$ for the reaction $CHCl_3 + Cl = CCl_3 + HCl$.

(e) The values at the δ or γ positions (bracketed) are assumed the same as for the 2 position in *n*-butane (ref. 14). The other values are calculated relative to this. These results must be considered very approximate.

(f) Estimated from thermodynamic data.

(g) *A* factor is assumed to be 10^{14}.

(h) Calculated from the reverse reaction.

(i) Estimated assuming $k = 10^{13.42} \exp(-3850/RT)$ for the reaction $CH_4 + Cl = CH_3 + HCl$.

(j) Estimated assuming $k = 10^{13.96} \exp(-1040/RT)$ for the reaction $C_2H_6 + Cl = C_2H_5 + HCl$.

References (Chlorine Atoms)

1. Hertel, Z. Phys. Chem. **15B,** 325 (1931).
2. Potts and Rollefson, J. Am. Chem. Soc. **57,** 1027 (1935).
3. Rodebush and Klingelhoefer, J. Am. Chem. Soc. **55,** 130 (1933).
4. Steiner and Rideal, Proc. Roy. Soc. **173A,** 503 (1939).
5. Ashmore and Chanmugam, Trans. Faraday Soc. **49,** 254 (1953).
6. Ashmore, 5th Int. Comb. Symp., p. 700 (Reinhold, N.Y., 1955).
7. Fettis and Knox, Progress in Reaction Kinetics, Vol. 2, p. 3 (Pergamon Press, N.Y., 1964).
8. Bigeleisen, Klein, Weston, and Wolfsberg, J. Chem. Phys. **30,** 1340 (1959).
9. Jones, J. Chem. Phys. **19,** 78 (1951).
10. Rollefson, J. Chem. Phys. **2,** 144 (1934).
11. Rollefson, J. Am. Chem. Soc. **56,** 579 (1934).
12. Chiltz, Eckling, Goldfinger, Huybrechts, Johnston, Meyers, and Verbecke, J. Chem. Phys. **38,** 1053 (1963).
13. Pritchard, Pyke, and Trotman-Dickenson. J. Am. Chem. Soc. **76,** 1201 (1954).
14. Knox and Nelson, Trans. Faraday Soc. **55,** 937 (1959).
15. Knox, Chem. and Ind. 1631 (1955).
16. Pritchard, Pyke, and Trotman-Dickenson, J. Am. Chem. Soc. **77,** 2629 (1955).
17. Anson, Fredricks, and Tedder, J. Chem. Soc. 918 (1959).
18. Knox, Trans. Faraday Soc. **58,** 275 (1962).
19. Goldfinger, Huybrechts, and Martens, Trans. Faraday Soc. **57,** 2210 (1961).
20. Chiltz, Martens, and Mahieu, Nature **180,** 1068 (1957).
21. Chiltz, Mahieu, and Martens, Bull. Soc. Chim. Belges **67,** 33 (1958).
22. Newton and Rollefson, J. Chem. Phys. **17,** 718 (1949).
23. Chiltz, Goldfinger, Huybrechts, Martens, and Verbeke, Chem. Rev. **63,** 355 (1963).
24. Ackerman, Chiltz, Goldfinger, and Martens, Bull. Soc. Chim. Belges **66,** 325 (1957).
25. Galiba, Tedder, and Watson, J. Chem. Soc. 1321 (1964).
26. Fredricks and Tedder, J. Chem. Soc. 144 (1960).
27. Ashmore and Spencer, Trans. Faraday Soc. **60,** 1608 (1964).
28. Goldfinger, Jeunehomme, and Martens, J. Chem. Phys. **29,** 456 (1958).

29. Fredricks and Tedder, Chem. and Ind. 490 (1959).
30. Eckling, Goldfinger, Huybrechts, Martens, Meyers, and Smoes, Chem. Ber. **93,** 3014 (1960).
31. Huybrechts, Meyers, and Verbeke, Trans. Faraday Soc. **58,** 1128 (1962).
32. Christie, Roy, and Thrush, Trans. Faraday Soc. **55,** 1139 (1959).
33. Christie, Roy, and Thrush, Trans. Faraday Soc. **55,** 1149 (1959).
34. Schofield, Tsang, and Bauer, J. Chem. Phys. **42,** 2132 (1965).
35. Burns and Dainton, Trans. Faraday Soc. **48,** 52 (1952).
36. Burns and Dainton, Trans. Faraday Soc. **48,** 39 (1952).
37. Kaufman, Gerri, and Pascale, J. Chem. Phys. **24,** 32 (1956).
38. Tamura, Rev. Phys. Chem. Japan. **11,** 1 (1937).
39. Klein, Persky, and Weston, J. Chem. Phys. **41,** 1799 (1964).
40. Edgecombe, Norrish, and Thrush, Proc. Roy. Soc. **243A,** 24 (1957).
41. Persky and Klein, J. Chem. Phys. **44,** 3617 (1966).
42. Polanyi, "Atomic Reactions" (Williams and Norgate, London, 1932).
43. Bodenstein, Brenschede, and Schumacher, Z. Phys. Chem **40B,** 121 (1938).

Reviews

1. Chiltz, Goldfinger, Huybrechts, Martens, and Verbecke, Chem. Rev. **63,** 355 (1963).
2. Fettis and Knox, "Progress in Reaction Kinetics," Vol. 2, p. 3 (Pergamon Press, London, 1964).

Metathetical Reactions of Bromine Atoms

Reactants	Notes	E	$\log_{10}A$	Temperature range	Radical source	References
			HYDROGEN ATOM TRANSFER			
Hydrogen		*(kcal mole^{-1})*	*(cm^3 mole^{-1} sec^{-1})*	°C		
H_2		19.4 ± 0.2	14.36	227–302	H_2/Br_2 T	1, 2
		18.6 ± 0.6	13.93	277–327	H_2/Br_2 T	3, 2
		17.6	13.86	200–300	H_2/Br_2 P	4
	(a)	19.8	13.36	700–1400		6
		$k=(0.89$ and $1.03)\times10^{11}$		1123	H_2/Br_2 T	7
		$k=(0.91$ and $0.79)\times10^{11}$		1168	H_2/Br_2 T	7
	(b)	17.8	13.7			18
		18.3	14.03	327–1197	H_2/Br_2 T	8
		19.2 ± 1.8	14.25	1027–1427	H_2/Br_2 T	2
	(b)	19.7 ± 0.4	14.43 ± 0.14	227–1427		9
		19.17	14.24	832–1011	$H_2/O_2/CF_3Br$ ignition	32
		19.7	14.43			
HD	(i)	20.3	14.37	168–350	$HD/H_2/Br_2$ T, P	34
HT	(i)	20.4	14.34	168–350	$HT/H_2/Br_2$ T, P	34
D_2		20.2	14.89	277–377	H_2/Br_2 T	3, 2
		20.4 ± 1.0	14.08	1027–1427	H_2/Br_2 T	2
	(i)	21.0	14.31	168–350	$H_2/D_2/Br$ T, P	34
	(b)	21.4 ± 0.4	14.29	277–1427		9
		21.4	14.29			
Alkanes						
CH_4		18.2 ± 0.5	13.8	150–210	CH_4/Br_2 P	10
	(c) (d)	18.3	14.0	204–341	$CH_4/CH_3Cl/Br_2$ T, P	11
		17.3	13.15	150–300		22
		18.2	13.8			
C_2H_6		13.6 ± 0.5		35–90	C_2H_6/Br_2 P	13
	(d)	13.4 ± 0.1	13.90 ± 0.04	59–199	$C_2H_6/CH_3Br/Br_2$ T	11, 14
	(e)	12.3	13.29	25–121	$CH_3CHF_2/C_2H_6/$ Br_2 T	15
C_3H_8	(d)	10.15 ± 0.14	13.71 ± 0.07	13–145	$C_3H_8/C_2H_6/Br_2$ T	11, 14
n-C_4H_{10}	(d)	10.23 ± 0.23	13.22 ± 0.14	−6–98	n-C_4H_{10}/i-$C_4H_{10}/$ Br_2 T	11, 14, 20
i-C_4H_{10}	(d)	7.51 ± 0.20	13.30 ± 0.11	34–148	i-$C_4H_{10}/C_3H_8/Br_2$ T	11, 14, 20
	(h)	11.7	17.6	40–95	i-C_4H_{10}/Br_2 P	16, 17
neo-C_5H_{12}	(d)	14.29 ± 0.13	14.24 ± 0.06	57–200	neo$C_5H_{12}/C_2H_6/Br_2$ T	11
	(h)	18.2	17.0	98–152	neo-C_5H_{12}/Br_2 P	19, 17
Aromatic hydrocarbon						
$C_6H_5CH_3$	(h)	7.6	13.5	82–132	$C_6H_5CH_3/Br_2$ P	21, 25, 17
Halogenated alkanes						
CH_3F	(e)	14.8	12.86	150–300	$CH_4/CH_3F/Br_2$ P	12
CH_2F_2	(e)	15.3	12.52	150–300	$CH_4/CH_2F_2/Br_2$ P	12

Metathetical Reactions of Bromine Atoms – Continued

Reactants	Notes	E	$\log_{10}A$	Temperature range	Radical source	References
		(*kcal mole*$^{-1}$)	(*cm*^{3} *mole*$^{-1}$ *sec*$^{-1}$)	°C		
CHF_3	(e)	21.1	12.28	150–300	$CHF_3/C_2F_5H/Br_2$ P	12
		23.0	13.46	361–431	CF_3H/Br_2 T	22
CH_3Cl		14.45 ± 0.16	13.62 ± 0.06	59–200	$CH_3Cl/C_2H_6/Br_2$ T, P	11
$CHCl_3$		9.3	12.36	147–182	$CHCl_3/Br_2$ T	23, 17
		10.			$CHCl_3/Br_2$ P	24
CH_3Br		16.05	13.7	150–230	CH_3Br/Br_2 P	10, 11, 14
$CH_3C\mathbf{H}_2F$	(e)	10.3	12.38	39–121	$C_2H_6/C_2H_5F/Br_2$ P	15
$CH_3C\mathbf{H}F_2$	(e)	13.3	12.52	96–230	$CH_4/C_2H_4F_2/Br_2$ P	15
CH_3CF_3	(e)	22.2	13.18	243–379	$CF_3H/CH_3CF_3/Br_2$ P	15
CF_3CH_2F	(e)	18.2	12.73	130–322	$CH_2F_2/CF_3CH_2F/Br_2$ P	15
CF_2HCF_2H	(e)	18.1	12.75	118–283	$CH_2F_2/CF_3CH_2F/Br_2$ P	15
CF_3CF_2H	(e)	18.0	12.20	150–300	$CH_4/C_2F_5H/Br_2$	12
$CF_3CF_2CF_2H$		17.8	12.08	146–286	$CH_4/C_3F_7H/Br_2$ T	15
$CH_3CH_2CH_2C\mathbf{H}_2F$	(f)	11.6	13.2	62–185	$CH_3CH_2CH_2CH_2F/Br_2$ P	26
$CH_3CH_2C\mathbf{H}_2CH_2F$	(f)	11.5	13.1	62–185	$CH_3CH_2CH_2CH_2F/Br_2$ P	26
$CH_3C\mathbf{H}_2CH_2CH_2F$	(f)	(10.2)	(13.6)	62–185	$CH_3CH_2CH_2CH_2F/Br_2$ P	26
$C\mathbf{H}_3CH_2CH_2CH_2F$	(f)	13.0	13.0	62–185	$CH_3CH_2CH_2CH_2F/Br_2$ P	26
$CF_3CH_2C\mathbf{H}_2CH_2CH_3$	(g) (f)	11.0	13.2	0–230	$CF_3CH_2CH_2CH_2CH_3/Br_2$ P	26
$CF_3CH_2CH_2C\mathbf{H}_2CH_3$	(f)	(10.2)	(13.6)	0–230	$CF_3CH_2CH_2CH_2CH_3/Br_2$ P	26
$CF_3CH_2CH_2CH_2C\mathbf{H}_3$	(f)	13.0	13.1	0–230	$CF_3CH_2CH_2CH_2CH_3/Br_2$ P	26
Alcohols						
$\mathbf{CH_3}OH$		6.3	11.65	76–135	CH_3OH/Br_2 P	27
CH_3CH_2OH		2.6 ± 2.0		70–150	C_2H_5OH/Br_2 P	28

CHLORINE ATOM TRANSFER

Reactants	Notes	E	$\log_{10}A$	Temperature range	Radical source	References
Cl_2		6.9 ± 0.4	12.65 ± 0.2	20–60	Br_2/Cl_2 P	29

BROMINE ATOM TRANSFER

Reactants	Notes	E	$\log_{10}A$	Temperature range	Radical source	References
Alkyl halides						
CH_3Br		22.9	13.7	150–297	CH_4/Br_2 P, T	10, 17
CH_2Br_2			14.0			10, 17

Reactants	Notes	E	$\log_{10}A$	Temperature range	Radical source		References
		(*kcal mole*$^{-1}$)	(*cm*^{3} *mole*$^{-1}$ *sec*$^{-1}$)	°*C*			
CCl_3Br		10.3	13.91	146–183	CCl_3Br/Br_2	T	30
Hydrogen halide							
HBr	(a)	43.8 41.7	14.4 13.9	700–1400 25–302	H_2/Br_2	T	6 33, 17
Halogen							
BrCl		$k=(3.1\pm0.8)\times10^{3}$		20	Br_2/Cl_2	P	29
OXYGEN ATOM TRANSFER							
N_2O		37	14.3	603–700	N_2O/Br_2	T	31
MISCELLANEOUS REACTIONS							
$Br+Na_2=NaBr+Na$		$k=1.5\times10^{14}$		~ 300	Br_2/Na	D.F.	35

Notes

(a) Estimated from a general review of kinetic data.

(b) Critical survey of literature data.

(c) These values are less reliable than those given for other compounds, by the same authors.

(d) All values are related to $Br+CH_3Br=CH_2Br+HBr$ as standard, for which $k=10^{13.73}\exp(-16050/RT)$.

(e) Measured relative to $CH_4+Br=CH_3+HBr$ for which $k=10^{13.15}\exp(-17300/RT)$. This is a recalculation of data from ref. 10. To compare these values with the others, E should be increased by 1 kcal/mole and log A by 0.65 units.

(f) The values at the δ or γ positions (bracketed) are assumed the same as for the 2 position in *n*-butane (ref. 11). The other values are calculated relative to this. These values must be considered very approximate.

(g) Very small quantities of $CF_3CHBrCH_2CH_2CH_3$ were formed, but not in sufficient quantities for the Arrhenius factors to be estimated.

(h) These values are believed to be in error (ref. 17)

(i) Measured relative to $Br+H_2=H+HBr$, for which $k=10^{14.43}\exp(-19{,}700/RT)$.

References (Bromine Atoms)

1. Bodenstein and Lind, Z. Phys. Chem. **57,** 168 (1906).
2. Britton and Cole, J. Phys. Chem. **65,** 1302 (1961).
3. Bach, Bonhoeffer, and Moelwyn-Hughes, Z. Phys. Chem. **27B,** 71 (1935).
4. Bodenstein and Lutkemeyer, Z. Phys. Chem. **114,** 208 (1924).
5. Steiner, Proc. Roy. Soc. **173A,** 531 (1939).
6. Cooley and Anderson, Ind. and Eng. Chem. **44,** 1402 (1952).
7. Britton and Davidson, J. Chem. Phys. **23,** 2461 (1955).
8. Levy, J. Phys. Chem. **62,** 570 (1958).
9. Fettis and Knox, Progress in Reaction Kinetics, Vol. 2, p. 3 (Pergamon Press, 1964).
10. Kistiakowsky and Van Artsdalen, J. Chem. Phys. **12,** 469 (1944).
11. Fettis, Knox, and Trotman-Dickenson, J. Chem. Soc. 4177 (1960).
12. Tarr, Coomber, and Whittle, Trans. Faraday Soc. **61,** 1182 (1965).
13. Andersen and Van Artsdalen, J. Chem. Phys. **12,** 479 (1944).
14. Fettis and Trotman-Dickenson, J. Am. Chem. Soc. **81,** 5260 (1959).
15. Coomber and Whittle, Trans. Faraday Soc. **62,** 1553 (1966).
16. Eckstein, Scheraga, and Van Artsdalen, J. Chem. Phys. **22,** 28 (1954).
17. Benson and Buss, J. Chem. Phys. **28,** 301 (1958).
18. Campbell and Fristom, Chem. Rev. **58,** 173 (1958).
19. Hormats and Van Artsdalen, J. Chem. Phys. **19,** 778 (1951).
20. Anson, Fredricks, and Tedder, J. Chem. Soc. 918 (1959).
21. Anderson, Scheraga, and Van Artsdalen, J. Chem. Phys. **21,** 1258 (1953).
22. Corbett, Tarr, and Whittle, Trans. Faraday Soc. **59,** 1609 (1963).
23. Sullivan and Davidson, J. Chem. Phys. **19,** 143 (1951).
24. Braunworth and Schumacher, Kolloidzschr. **89,** 184 (1939).
25. Swegler, Scheraga, and Van Artsdalen, J. Chem. Phys. **19,** 135 (1951).
26. Galiba, Tedder, and Watson, J. Chem. Soc. 1321 (1964).
27. Buckley and Whittle, Trans. Faraday Soc. **58,** 536 (1962).
28. Tarr and Whittle, Trans. Faraday Soc. **60,** 2039 (1964).
29. Christie and Thrush, Trans. Faraday Soc. **55,** 1139 (1959).
30. Davidson and Sullivan, J. Chem. Phys. **17,** 176 (1949).
31. Kaufman, Gerri, and Pascale, J. Chem. Phys. **24,** 32 (1956).
32. Skinner and Ringrose, J. Chem. Phys. **43,** 4129 (1965).
33. Bodenstein and Jung, Z. Phys. Chem. **121,** 127 (1926).
34. Timmons and Weston, J. Chem. Phys. **41,** 1654 (1964).
35. Polanyi, "Atomic Reactions." (Williams and Norgate, London, 1932).

Review

1. Fettis and Knox, "Progress in Reaction Kinetics," Vol. 2, p. 3 (Pergamon Press, London, 1964).

Metathetical Reactions of Iodine Atoms

Reactants	Notes	E	$\log_{10}A$	Temperature range	Radical source	References
		HYDROGEN ATOM TRANSFER				
Hydrogen		(*kcal mole*$^{-1}$)	(*cm*^{3} *mole*$^{-1}$ *sec*$^{-1}$)	°C		
H_2		33.9 ± 0.3	14.32 ± 0.11	105–360	H_2/I_2 T	1
		33.5 ± 0.2	14.20 ± 0.07	394–527	H_2/I_2 T	2
		$k = 4.6 \times 10^6$		700	HI and H_2/I_2 T	3, 4
D_2		34.5 ± 0.3	14.06 ± 0.10	394–527	D_2/I_2 T	5
Alkanes						
CH_4	(a)	33.5	14.70	260–316		6, 7
		34.1	14.70	260–316	CH_4/I_2 T	7
		35.0 ± 1.1	14.95	275–345	CH_4/I_2 T	8
C_2H_6		27.9	14.22	263–303	C_2H_5I/HI T	9
C_3H_8		25.5 ± 1	14.53 ± 0.36	307–340	C_3H_8/I_2 T	10
$CH_3\mathbf{CH_2}CH_3$		25.0	14.22	307–340	C_3H_8/I_2 T	10
i-C_4H_{10}		21.4 ± 0.5	13.88 ± 0.15	252–310	*i*-C_4H_{10}/I_2 T	11
Alkenes						
$CH_2{:}CH\mathbf{CH_3}$		18.04 ± 0.32	13.25 ± 0.14	208–300	$CH_2{:}CHCH_3/I_2$ T	22
1-$CH_2{:}CHCH_2CH_3$		13.2 ± 0.4	12.83 ± 0.15	204–253	$CH_2{:}CHCH_2CH_3/I_2$ T	12
Aromatic hydrocarbon						
$C_6H_5CH_3$		$k = 4.8 \times 10^7$		501	$C_6H_5I/C_6H_5CH_3$ T	13
Aldehyde						
CH_3CHO		15.7	13.3	222–268	CH_3COI/HI T	14
Alcohol						
$(CH_3)_2\mathbf{CH}OH$		20.5	14.07	207–300	$(CH_3)_2CHOH/I_2$ T	23
		IODINE ATOM TRANSFER				
Alkyl halides						
CH_3I		19.8	14.3	270–320	CH_3I/HI T	15, 16
		$\geqslant 20.5$	($k = 1.60 \times 10^3$)	280	CH_3I/HI T	17, 16
		20.5 ± 0.5	14.4 ± 0.2	260–316	CH_3I/HI T	6
		19.2	13.71		CH_3I/HI T	18
CF_3I		17.60	13.8	167–485	CF_3I/HI T	18
C_2H_5I		16.7	13.62	250–300	C_2H_5I/HI T	15, 16
		$\geqslant 18.2$	($k = 6.8 \times 10^3$)	260	C_2H_5I/HI T	17, 16
		17.1 ± 0.7	14.01 ± 0.28	263–303	C_2H_5I/HI T	9
n-C_3H_7I		$\geqslant 18.5$	($k = 12.9 \times 10^3$)	290	*n*-C_3H_7I/HI T	17, 16
$ICH_2CH_2CH_2I$		19.5	14.0			19
$(CH_3)_3CI$		13.0 ± 0.7	13.7 ± 0.4	252–310	$(CH_3)_3CH/I_2$ T	11

Metathetical Reactions of Iodine Atoms—Continued

Reactants	Notes	E	$\log_{10}A$	Temperature range	Radical source		References
		(*kcal mole*$^{-1}$)	(*cm*^{3} *mole*$^{-1}$ *sec*$^{-1}$)	°C			
Acetyl halide							
CH_3COI		14.6	13.9	222–268	CH_3COI/HI	T	14
Hydrogen halide							
HI		36.4	14.32 ± 0.20	105–360	H_2/I_2	T	1
		36.5		394–527	H_2/I_2	T	2
OXYGEN ATOM TRANSFER							
N_2O		38	14.45	603–700	N_2O/I_2	T	20
MISCELLANEOUS REACTIONS							
$I + Na_2 = NaI + Na$		$k = 2.6 \times 10^{13}$		~300	I_2/Na	D.F.	21

Notes

(a) Calculated from the reverse reaction.
(b) Estimated from thermodynamic data.

References (Iodine Atoms)

1. Sullivan, J. Chem. Phys. **30,** 1292 (1959).
2. Sullivan, J. Chem. Phys. **36,** 1925 (1962).
3. Horie, Ishii, and Amano, J. Phys. Chem. **68,** 1264 (1964).
4. Graven, J. Am. Chem. Soc. **78,** 3297 (1956).
5. Sullivan, J. Chem. Phys. **39,** 3001 (1963).
6. Flowers and Benson, J. Chem. Phys. **38,** 882 (1963).
7. Golden, Walsh, and Benson. J. Am. Chem. Soc. **87,** 4053 (1965).
8. Goy and Pritchard, J. Phys. Chem. **69,** 3040 (1965).
9. Hartley and Benson, J. Chem. Phys. **39,** 132 (1963).
10. Nangia and Benson, J. Am. Chem. Soc. **86,** 2773 (1964).
11. Teranishi and Benson, J. Am. Chem. Soc. **85,** 2887 (1963).
12. Benson, Bose, and Nangia, J. Am. Chem. Soc. **85,** 1388 (1963).
13. Yang and Conway, J. Chem. Phys. **43,** 1296 (1965).
14. O'Neal and Benson, J. Chem. Phys. **37,** 540 (1962).
15. Sullivan, J. Phys. Chem. **65,** 722 (1961).
16. Ogg, J. Am. Chem. Soc. **56,** 526 (1934).
17. Benson and O'Neal, J. Chem. Phys. **34,** 514 (1961).
18. Body, Downs, Gow, and Horrex, J. Phys. Chem. **67,** 719 (1963).
19. Benson, J. Chem. Phys. **34,** 521 (1961).
20. Kaufman, Gerri, and Pascale, J. Chem. Phys. **24,** 32 (1956).
21. Polanyi, "Atomic Reactions" (Williams and Norgate, London, 1932).
22. Golden, Rodgers, and Benson, J. Am. Chem. Soc. **88,** 3196 (1966).
23. Walsh and Benson, J. Am. Chem. Soc. **88,** 3480 (1966).

Review

1. Fettis and Knox, "Progress in Reaction Kinetics," Vol. 2, p. 3 (Pergamon Press, London, 1964).

Ratios of Rate Constants (Sulphur Atoms)

Reactions	Notes	$E_1 - E_2$	$\log_{10}A_1/A_2$	k_1/k_2	Temperature Range	Radical Source	References
		(*kcal mole*$^{-1}$)			°*C*		
(1) $S(^1D) + COS = CO + S_2$ (2) $S(^1D) + CH_4 = CH_3SH$				17.8	25	COS P	1
(1) $S(^1D) + COS = CO + S_2$ (2) $S(^1D) + C_2H_6 = C_2H_5SH$	(a)			2.2 2.04	25 25	COS P COS P	2 1
(1) $S(^1D) + COS = CO + S_2$ (2) $S(^1D) + C_3H_8 = C_3H_7SH$				1.9	25	COS P	2
(1) $S(^1D) + COS = CO + S_2$ (2) $S(^1D) + i\text{-}C_4H_{10} = C_4H_9SH$				2.04	25	COS P	1

Notes

(a) Ratio decreases with pressure.

(b) Data also given (ref. 2) on S atom insertion into cyclo-C_3H_6, cyclo-C_4H_8, and cyclo-C_5H_{10}.

References

1. Knight, Strauss, and Gunning, J. Am. Chem. Soc. **85,** 2349 (1963).
2. Knight, Strauss, Malm, and Gunning, J. Am. Chem. Soc. **86,** 4243 (1964).

247-168 O-67—3

Reactions of Sodium Atoms

Index

Metathetical Reactions of Sodium Atoms

Reactants	Notes	(a) E	$\log_{10} k$	Temperature range	Radical source	References
			FLUORINE ATOM TRANSFER			
Halogenated alkanes		(*kcal mole*$^{-1}$)	(*cm*^{3} *mole*$^{-1}$ *sec*$^{-1}$)	°C		
CF_2	(b) (e)		$6.5 \log (k_f)^{1/2}$	313	D.F.	4
	(e)		$5.0 \log (k_f)^{1/2}$	310	D.F.	5
CFH_2	(b) (c)		$6.1 \log (k_e)^{1/2}$	313	D.F.	4
CF_2H	(b) (d)		$6.2 \log (k_c)^{1/2}$	313	D.F.	4
CF_3	(b)		13.83	313	D.F.	4
			13.97	310	D.F.	5
CFH_3		> 25	< 8.7	240	D.F.	1, 6
		~ 18.5	7.3	247		2, 3
CH_2F_2		14.0	8.8	247		2, 3
CHF_3		14.0	8.8	247		2, 3
CF_4		12.6	9.4	247		2, 3
cyclo-C_6F_{12}		7.1	11.7	247		2, 3
cyclo-$C_6F_{11}CF_3$		6.7	12.0	247		2, 3
Alkenes						
C_2F_4		8.8	11.0	247		2, 3
Acids and acid halides						
CF_3COOH		4.0	13.0	247		2, 3
CF_3COF		7.6	11.5	247		2, 3
Halogenated aromatics						
C_6H_5F			< 8.7	247		19
Miscellaneous						
SF_6		3.3	13.3	247		2, 3
			CHLORINE ATOM TRANSFER			
Halogenated alkanes						
CH_3Cl		7.5	10.7	240	D.F.	1, 6
			10.9	270		7
			11.8	325	M.D.F.	8
	(f)	9.8	11.1	313	D.F.	9
		8.2			D.F.	10
			11.8	220	M.L.	11

Metathetical Reactions of Sodium Atoms – Continued

Reactants	Notes	(a) E	$\log_{10} k$	Temperature range	Radical source	References
		(*kcal mole*$^{-1}$)	(*cm*^{3} *mole*$^{-1}$ *sec*$^{-1}$)	°C		
CH_2Cl_2			11.75	275	D.F.	1, 6
			12.4	270		7
			11.8	250	D.F.	12
$CHCl_3$			12.7	275	D.F.	1, 6
			13.5	270		7
			13.0	250	D.F.	12
CCl_4			13.3	275	D.F.	1, 6
			14.5	270		7
			14.0	250	D.F.	12
	(g) (f)	8.4	12.17	310	M.D.F.	13
			14.35	247	D.F.	14
CH_2FCl	(g) (f)	10.1	10.97	313	D.F.	9
CHF_2Cl			10.0	247		3
	(g) (f)	10.0	11.0	313	D.F.	9
CF_3Cl			10.7	247		3
		9.2	11.3	313	D.F.	9
	(f)	7.4		275–315	D.F.	15
	(g) (f)	10.2	10.9	310	M.D.F.	13
CF_2Cl_2	(g) (f)	9.0 to 9.5	11.5 to 11.7	310	M.D.F.	13
$CFCl_3$	(g) (f)	8.7 to 9.2	11.8 to 11.9	310	M.D.F.	13
C_2H_5Cl			10.9	275	D.F.	6, 1
		10.2		260–380	D.F.	16, 17
		7.8		292–391	D.F.	10
CH_2ClCH_2Cl			11.8	275	D.F.	6
	(a)	7.0	12.0	285	D.F.	18
CH_3CHCl_2			11.9	275	D.F.	6
CH_3CCl_3			13.6	247	D.F.	14
$CH_3CH_2CH_2Cl$	(a)	9.1	11.1	275	D.F.	6
	(a)	9.0	11.0	261	D.F.	18
			10.7	267	D.F.	19
$CH_3CHClCH_3$			11.2	275	D.F.	6
$CH_2ClCH_2CH_2Cl$			11.7	275	D.F.	6
$CH_3CHClCH_2Cl$			12.0	275	D.F.	6
$CH_3CH_2CHCl_2$			12.2	275	D.F.	6
$(CH_3)_2CCl_2$			12.4	275	D.F.	6
			12.6	247	D.F.	14
$CH_3CH_2CH_2CH_2Cl$			11.2	275	D.F.	6
$CH_3CH_2CHClCH_3$			11.4	275	D.F.	6

Metathetical Reactions of Sodium Atoms – Continued

Reactants	Notes	(a) E	$\log_{10} k$	Temperature range	Radical source	References
		(kcal mole⁻¹)	*(cm³ mole⁻¹ sec⁻¹)*	°C		
$(CH_3)_2CHCH_2Cl$			11.2	275	D.F.	6
$(CH_3)_3CCl$			11.5	275	D.F.	6
			11.4	247	D.F.	14
$CH_3CH_2CH_2CH_2CH_2Cl$			11.4	275	D.F.	6
$(CH_3)_2CHCH_2CH_2Cl$			11.4	275	D.F.	6
$(CH_3)_2CClCH_2CH_3$			11.9	275	D.F.	6
Alkenes						
CH_2:CHCl			10.7	275	D.F.	6
trans-CHCl:CHCl			11.3	275	D.F.	6
cis-CHCl:CHCl			11.4	275	D.F.	6
$CH_2:CHCH_2Cl$			12.3	275	D.F.	6
			12.5	260	D.F.	18
$CH_2:CClCH_3$			11.0	275	D.F.	6
C_6H_5CH:CHCl			13.0	275	D.F.	18
$C_6H_5CH:CHCH_2Cl$			13.9	275	D.F.	18
Aromatic chlorides and their derivatives						
C_6H_5Cl			9.4	247	D.F.	19
			11.2	244	M.L.	25
			11.8	270	D.F.	1
$C_6H_5CH_2Cl$			14.7	275	D.F.	6
			13.7	284	D.F.	18
$C_6H_5CH_2CH_2Cl$			13.4	285	D.F.	18
o-FC_6H_4Cl			10.3	247	D.F.	19
m-FC_6H_4Cl			9.8	247	D.F.	19
p-FC_6H_4Cl			9.1	247	D.F.	19
o-ClC_6H_4Cl			11.2	247	D.F.	19
o-$CH_3OOCC_6H_4Cl$			13.4	247	D.F.	19
2:Cl-pyridine			12.7	247	D.F.	19
3:Cl-pyridine			10.0	247	D.F.	19
Cyanides						
$CNCH_2Cl$			13.9	285	D.F.	18

Metathetical Reactions of Sodium Atoms—Continued

Reactants	Notes	(a) E	$\log_{10} k$	Temperature range	Radical source	References
		(kcal mole^{-1})	*(cm^3 mole^{-1} sec^{-1})*	°C		
$CNCH_2CH_2Cl$			11.8	285	D.F.	18
Acids, acid chlorides, esters, etc.						
$CH_2ClCOOH$			13.3	247		3
CH_3COCl			12.7	275	D.F.	6, 1
			13.4	247	D.F.	3, 2
		0			D.F.	10
C_6H_5COCl			14.7	240	D.F.	1
$ClCOOC_2H_5$			11.6	247	D.F.	3, 2
$CH_2ClCOOC_2H_5$			13.2	247	D.F.	3, 2
$ClCH_2CH_2OH$			11.7	285	D.F.	18
CH_3COCH_2Cl			13.7	275	D.F.	6
			14.0	247	D.F.	2
CH_3OCH_2Cl			11.3	247		3, 2
Polyhalides						
BCl_3			11.7	270	D.F.	7
$SiCl_4$			11.6	270	D.F.	7
			11.8	247	D.F.	14
CH_3SiCl_3			9.8	247	D.F.	14
$(CH_3)_2SiCl_2$			9.3	247	D.F.	14
$(CH_3)_3SiCl$			9.4	247	D.F.	14
PCl_3			14.2	270	D.F.	7
$TiCl_4$			14.0	270	D.F.	7
$GeCl_4$			14.7	270	D.F.	7
$AsCl_3$			14.2	270	D.F.	7
$SnCl_4$			14.5	270	D.F.	7
SCl_2			14.8	270	D.F.	7
S_2Cl_2			14.2	270	D.F.	7
Oxychlorides						
$COCl_2$			13.9	270	D.F.	7
CrO_2Cl_2			14.1	270	D.F.	7
$POCl_3$			14.4	270	D.F.	7

Metathetical Reactions of Sodium Atoms—Continued

Reactants	Notes	(a) E	$\log_{10} k$	Temperature range	Radical source	References
		(*kcal mole*$^{-1}$)	(*cm*^{3} *mole*$^{-1}$ *sec*$^{-1}$)	°*C*		
Halogens and pseudo-halogens						
Cl_2			14.6		Dil. F.	20
CNCl			14.0	285	D.F.	18
			13.9	250	D.F.	1
Hydrogen halide						
HCl			12.4	327	Dil. F.	21, 20

BROMINE ATOM TRANSFER

Reactants	Notes	(a) E	$\log_{10} k$	Temperature range	Radical source	References
[alogenated alkanes						
CH_3Br			13.3	240	D.F.	1, 6
			12.8	270		7
			12.6	255	D.F.	12
			12.2	200	M.L.	11
			12.8	242	M.L.	11
	(h)	3.4				10
CH_2Br_2			13.6	255	D.F.	12
			13.5	255	M.L.	12
$CHBr_3$			14.6	255	D.F.	12
			13.9	255	M.L.	12
$CFBr_3$			14.3	255	D.F.	12
CF_3Br	(a)	2.3		285	D.F.	15
$CHFBr_2$			13.7	255	M.L.	12
CH_2ClBr			13.3	255	D.F.	12
			13.3	255	M.L.	12
$CHClBr_2$			14.3	255	D.F.	12
			13.7	255	M.L.	12
$CHCl_2Br$			14.0	255	D.F.	12
			13.6	255	M.L.	12
CCl_3Br			14.5	255	D.F.	12
			14.0	255	M.L.	12
C_2H_5Br			12.8	240	D.F.	1
			12.4	247	D.F.	19
			12.7	263	D.F.	18

Metathetical Reactions of Sodium Atoms—Continued

Reactants	Notes	(a) E	$\log_{10} k$	Temperature range	Radical source	References
		($kcal\ mole^{-1}$)	($cm^3\ mole^{-1}\ sec^{-1}$)	°C		
CH_2BrCH_2Br			13.3	247		3
cyclo-C_3H_5Br			12.0	247	D.F.	22
cyclo-C_4H_7Br			12.6	247	D.F.	22
cyclo-C_5H_9Br			13.1	247	D.F.	22
$CH_3CH_2CH_2CH_2CH_2Br$			12.8	247	D.F.	22
cyclo-$C_6H_{11}Br$			12.7			23
			12.7	247	D.F.	22
Alkenes						
$CH_2{:}CHBr$			12.4	269	D.F.	18
			11.2	247	D.F.	22
$C_6H_5CH{:}CHBr$			13.1	270	D.F.	18
$C_6H_5CH{:}CHCH_2Br$			14.6	285	D.F.	18
Aromatic bromides and their derivatives						
C_6H_5Br			12.3	255	M.L.	24
			11.4	247	D.F.	19
			13.2	244	M.L.	25
			13.4	260	D.F.	1
			12.1	247	D.F.	14
o-ClC_6H_4Br			12.6	247	D.F.	19
m-ClC_6H_4Br			11.9	247	D.F.	19
p-ClC_6H_4Br			11.6	247	D.F.	19
o-BrC_6H_4Br			13.4	247	D.F.	19
o-CNC_6H_4Br			13.3	247	D.F.	19
m-CNC_6H_4Br			12.6	247	D.F.	19
p-CNC_6H_4Br			12.8	247	D.F.	19
o-HOC_6H_4Br			12.2	247	D.F.	19
m-HOC_6H_4Br			11.8	247	D.F.	19
o-$CH_3C_6H_4Br$			11.5	247	D.F.	19
m-$CH_3C_6H_4Br$			11.2	247	D.F.	19

Metathetical Reactions of Sodium Atoms—Continued

Reactants	Notes	[(a)] E	$\log_{10} k$	Temperature range	Radical source	References
		(*kcal mole*$^{-1}$)	(*cm*^{3} *mole*$^{-1}$ *sec*$^{-1}$)	°C		
p-$CH_3C_6H_4Br$			11.3	247	D.F.	19
o-$CH_3OC_6H_4Br$			11.9	247	D.F.	19
p-$CH_3OC_6H_4Br$			11.6	247	D.F.	19
o-$CH_3OOC_6H_4Br$			13.8	247	D.F.	19
m-$CH_3OOC_6H_4Br$			12.6	247	D.F.	19
p-$CH_3OOC_6H_4Br$			12.6	247	D.F.	19
α-Bromonaphthalene			12.7	247		3
β-Bromonaphthalene			12.1	247		3
2:Br-pyridine			13.3	247	D.F.	19
3:Br-pyridine			11.9	247	D.F.	19
$C_6H_5CH_2CH_2Br$			13.6	280	D.F.	18
Acid bromide						
CH_3COBr			13.9	300	D.F.	1
Halogens and pseudohalogens						
CNBr			14.1	273	D.F.	18
Hydrogen halide						
HBr			13.8	327	Dil. F.	21, 20
IODINE ATOM TRANSFER						
Halogenated alkanes						
CH_3I			14.7	240	D.F.	6
			14.5	240	M.L.	11
			13.7	250	M.L.	12
			13.6	255	D.F.	12
			13.6	277	D.F.	23
		0			D.F.	10
CF_3I			14.0	247		3
		1.7		285–295	D.F.	15
C_2H_5I			14.0	240–270	D.F.	1
			14.3	276	D.F.	18
$CH_3CH_2CH_2I$			13.4	240	D.F.	1

Metathetical Reactions of Sodium Atoms – Continued

Reactants	Notes	(a) E	$\log_{10} k$	Temperature range	Radical source	References
		(*kcal mole*$^{-1}$)	(*cm*^{3} *mole*$^{-1}$ *sec*$^{-1}$)	°*C*		
Alkenes						
CH_2:CHI			13.4	263	D.F.	18
Aromatic iodides						
C_6H_5I			14.7	240	D.F.	1
			14.3	244	M.L.	25
Halogens						
I_2			14.8		Dil. F.	20
Hydrogen halide						
HI			14.7	327	Dil. F.	20, 21
CYANIDE GROUP TRANSFER						
CH_3CN			< 6.6	247		3
$C_6H_5CH_2CN$			9.8	247		3
$CH_2(CN)COOC_2H_5$			11.6	247		3

Notes

(a) The activation energies E are calculated from the formula $k = 10^{14.7} \exp(-E/RT)$.

(b) These values are lower limits.

(c) k_e is the rate contant for the combination reaction $2CFH_2 = C_2F_2H_4$.

(d) k_c is the rate constant for the combination reaction $2CF_2H = C_2F_4H_2$.

(e) k_f is the rate constant for the combination reaction $2CF_2 = C_2F_4$.

(f) Calculated assuming a steric factor of unity.

(g) These values refer to the rate constants for the primary process.

(h) Estimated from a critical survey of literature data.

References

1. Von Hartel and Polanyi, Z. Phys. Chem. **11B,** 97 (1930).
2. Warhurst, Quart. Rev. Chem. Soc. **5,** 44 (1951).
3. Trotman-Dickenson, "Gas Kinetics," p. 219 (Butterworths, London, 1955).
4. Reed and Rabinovitch, J. Phys. Chem. **61,** 598 (1957).
5. Kaufman and Reed, J. Phys. Chem. **67,** 896 (1963).
6. Hartel, Meer, and Polanyi, Z. Phys. Chem. **19B,** 139 (1933).
7. Heller and Polanyi, Trans. Faraday Soc. **32,** 633 (1936).
8. Reed and Rabinovitch, J. Chem. Phys. **27,** 988 (1957).
9. Reed and Rabinovitch, J. Phys. Chem. **61,** 598 (1957).
10. Kerr, Lissi, and Trotman-Dickenson, J. Chem. Soc. 1673 (1964).
11. Frommer and Polanyi, Trans. Faraday Soc. **30,** 519 (1934).
12. Haresnape, Stevels, and Warhurst, Trans. Faraday Soc. **36,** 465 (1940).
13. Kaufman and Reed, J. Phys. Chem. **67,** 896 (1963).
14. Gowenlock and Thomas, J. Chem. Soc. 5068 (1965).
15. Hodgins and Haines, Can. J. Chem. **30,** 473 (1952).
16. Cvetanovic and Le Roy, J. Chem. Phys. **20,** 1016 (1952).
17. Cvetanovic and Le Roy, Can. J. Chem. **29,** 597 (1951).
18. Evans and Walker, Trans. Faraday Soc. **40,** 384 (1944).
19. Riding, Scanlon, and Warhurst, Trans. Faraday Soc. **52,** 1354 (1956).
20. Polanyi, "Atomic Reactions" (Williams and Norgate, London, 1932).
21. Schay, Z. Phys. Chem. **11B,** 291 (1930).
22. Friswell, Gowenlock, and Thomas, J. Chem. Soc. 6323 (1965).
23. Whittle (Ph. D. Thesis, Manchester, 1951).
24. Warhurst, Trans. Faraday Soc. **35,** 674 (1939).
25. Fairbrother and Warhurst, Trans. Faraday Soc. **31,** 987 (1935).

Reviews

1. Polanyi, "Atomic Reactions" (Williams and Norgate, London, 1932).
2. Bawn, Ann. Rep. Chem. Soc. **39,** 36 (1942).
3. Warhurst, Quart. Rev. Chem. Soc. **5,** 44 (1951).

Metathetical Reactions of Potassium Atoms

Reactants	Notes	E	$\log_{10} k$	Temperature range	Radical source	Reference
CHLORINE ATOM TRANSFER						
		(kcal mole)$^{-1}$	*(cm^3 mole^{-1} sec^{-1})*	°C		
HCl			14.0	327	Dil F.	1, 2
Cl_2	(b)					
BROMINE ATOM TRANSFER						
HBr			14.6	327	Dil F.	1, 2
	(a)	3.4			M.B.	3
Br_2	(b)					
IODINE ATOM TRANSFER						
HI			15.3	327	Dil F.	1, 2
CH_3I	(a)	< 0.3			M.B.	5

Notes

(a) These quantities cannot be identified with normal Arrhenius factors.

(b) See reference 4.

Ratios of Rate Constants (Potassium Atoms)

The table refers to ratios of rate constants for reactions of the following types:

$$K + R_1X = KX + R_1 \quad (1)$$

$$K + R_2X = KX + R_2 \quad (2)$$

where X is any halogen atom.

R_1X	R_2X	Notes	$E_1 - E_2$	A_2/A_1	k_2/k_1	Temperature range	Radical source	Reference
			(kcal mole^{-1})			°C		
CH_3Cl	C_2H_5Cl		0.4 ± 0.09	0.83 ± 0.10		217–333	D.F.	6
CH_3Cl	CH_3COCl				360	285	D.F.	6
C_2H_5Cl	$(CH_3)_2CHCl$		-0.13 ± 0.14	2.18 ± 0.25		238–325	D.F.	7
C_2H_5Cl	$(CH_3)_3CCl$		2.27 ± 0.55	0.78 ± 0.4		229–275	D.F.	7
CH_3Br	C_2H_5Cl		4.4	0.52		230–316	D.F.	6
CH_3Br	CH_3COCl		1.4	3.5		229–318	D.F.	6
CH_3I	C_2H_5Cl				38	285	D.F.	6
CH_3I	CH_3COCl		0	7.0		238–322	D.F.	6

References

1. Schay, Z. Phys. Chem. **11B,** 291 (1930).
2. Polanyi, "Atomic Reactions," p. 46 (Williams and Norgate. London, 1932).
3. Taylor and Datz, J. Chem. Phys. **23,** 1711 (1955).
4. Krocsak and Schay, Z. Phys. Chem. **19B,** 344 (1932).
5. Herschbach, Kwei, and Norris, J. Chem. Phys. **34,** 1842 (1961).
6. Kerr, Lissi, and Trotman-Dickenson, J. Chem. Soc. 1673 (1964).
7. Emovon and Lissi, J. Chem. Soc. 3509 (1964).

Metathetical Reactions of Methyne Radicals

Reaction	Notes	E	$\log_{10} A$	Tempera-ture range	Radical source	Reference
		(*kcal mole*$^{-1}$)	(*cm*^{3} *mole*$^{-1}$ *sec*$^{-1}$)	°C		
$CH + NH_3 = HCN + H_2 + H$		$k > 6 \times 10^{10}$		no indication	C_2H_2/NH_3 flames	1

Reference

(1) Safrany, Reeves, and Harteck, J. Am. Chem. Soc. **86,** 3160 (1964).

Ratios of Rate Constants (Methylene Radicals)

Reactions	Notes	$E_1 - E_2$	$\log_{10}A_1/A_2$	k_1/k_2	Temperature range	Radical source		Reference
		(*kcal mole*$^{-1}$)			°C			
(1) $CH_2+CH_2CO=C_2H_4+CO$	(a)			2.3	6–9			1
(2) $CH_2+CO=CH_2CO$	(b)			1.25	4–16	$CH_2CO/^{13}CO$	P	1
(1) $CH_2+CH_2CO=C_2H_4+CO$ (2) $CH_2+C_2H_4=C_3H_6$		4.8			28–81	CH_2CO/O_2	P	2
(1) $CH_2+CH_2CO=C_2H_4+CO$ (2) $CH_2+C_2H_2=C_3H_4$	(c)			0.9 ± 0.1	no indication	CH_2CO/C_2H_2	F.P.	3
(1) $CH_2+CH_2CO=C_2H_4+CO$ (2) $CH_2+H_2=CH_3+H$		−0.8			−40–99	CH_2CO/H_2	P	4, 5, 7
(1) $CH_2+CH_2CO=C_2H_4+CO$ (2) $CH_2+CD_4=CH_2D_2+CD_2$		−0.9	0.15		27–298	CH_2CO/CD_4	P	6, 7

Notes

(a) and (b) represent two methods of estimating k_1/k_2: the discrepancy lies outside the experimental error.

(c) k_2 represents the sum of the rate constants for the reactions $CH_2+C_2H_2=HC{:}CCH_3$ and $CH_2+C_2H_2=H_2C{:}C{:}CH_2$.

References

1. Wilson and Kistiakowsky, J. Am. Chem. Soc. **80,** 2934 (1958).
2. Holroyd and Noyes, J. Am. Chem. Soc. **78,** 4831 (1956).
3. Terao, Sakai, and Shida, J. Am. Chem. Soc. **85,** 3919 (1963).
4. Gesser and Steacie, Can. J. Chem. **34,** 113 (1956).
5. Chanmugam and Burton, Can. J. Chem. **34,** 1021 (1956).
6. Chanmugam and Burton, J. Am. Chem. Soc. **78,** 509 (1956).
7. Bell and Kistiakowsky, J. Am. Chem. Soc. **84,** 3417 (1962).

Review

1. Frey, "Progress in Reaction Kinetics," Vol. 2, p. 133 (Pergamon Press, London, 1964).

Methyl Radical Reactions

Index

Metathetical Reactions of Methyl Radicals

Reactants	Notes	E	$\log_{10}A$	Temperature range	Radical source	References
			HYDROGEN ATOM TRANSFER			
Hydrogen		(*kcal mole*$^{-1}$)	(*cm*^{3} *mole*$^{-1}$ *sec*$^{-1}$)	°C		
H_2	(d)	10.0 ± 0.5	11.5	130–290	CH_3COCH_3 P	1, 2, 3
		9.9 ± 0.5	11.7	25–250	$Hg(CH_3)_2$ T	4, 3
		13 ± 2	13.4	50–250	$Cd(CH_3)_2$ P	5
	(a)	13.2 ± 1.0	12.5	136–318	CH_3COCH_3 P	6
		10.2 ± 0.5	11.52	99–207	CH_2CO P	7
	(b)	12.85	12.75			8
			$k = 4.1 \times 10^8$	507	CH_3OCH_3 T	9
		10.2	12.50	697–863	H_2/O_2 ignition	10
	(y)	10.2 ± 0.2	11.7	130–290	CD_3COCD_3 P	1, 2
	(y)	11.1	12.0	150–300	CD_3COCD_3 P	3
		10.0	11.5			
$\mathbf{H}D$		10.0	11.1	140–296	CH_3COCH_3 P	3
	(y)	10.7	11.4	137–298	CD_3COCD_3 P	3
$H\mathbf{D}$		11.5	11.5	135–296	CH_3COCH_3 P	3
	(y)	10.7	11.2	137–299	CD_3COCD_3 P	3
D_2	(d)	11.8 ± 0.1	11.8	130–290	CH_3COCH_3 P	1, 2, 3
	(c)	15.3 ± 1.0	14.8	258–451	CH_3CHO P	6
	(a)	14.3 ± 0.6	12.5	150–458	CH_3COCH_3 P	6
		12.7 ± 0.3	12.3	27–253	$Hg(CH_3)_2$ P	12
			$k = 2.0 \times 10^8$	507	CH_3OCH_3 T	9
		12.1 ± 0.6	11.79	151–299	CH_3COCH_3 P	13
		11.9	11.4	140–425	CH_3COCH_3 P	14
	(y)	10.9 ± 0.3	11.4	130–290	CD_3COCD_3 P	1, 2
Alkanes						
CH_4		14.9	12.00	200–350	CH_3COCH_3 P	16, 17
	(y)		$k = 1.7 \times 10^5$	182	CD_3COCD_3 P	18, 19
	(y)	14.3	11.5	350–525	CD_3COCD_3 P, T	20
	(y)		$k = 3.6 \times 10^6$	320	CD_3COCD_3 P	21
	(y)	14.1	11.8	200–350		17
$CH_3\mathbf{D}$	(y) (e)	12.8	10.42	27–327		22
$CD_3\mathbf{H}$	(e)	13.8	11.21	27–327		22
CD_4		12.93 ± 0.65	11.26	153–428	CH_3COCH_3 P	23, 17
	(y)	18.4	12.95	200–350	CD_3COCD_3 P	17
C_2H_6		12.0	10.6	770–890	C_2H_6 T	24
			$k = 1.4 \times 10^8$	630	C_2H_6 T	25
	(y) (f)	9.9 ± 1.1		500–560	CD_3CDO T	29, 51
	(y)	10.4 ± 0.4	11.3	116–294	CD_3COCD_3 P	19, 26
	(y)	11.8	12.21	162–341	CD_3COCD_3 P	21
	(y)	12.1	12.3	260–490	CD_3COCD_3 P	27
	(y)	11.5 ± 0.2	11.9	246–524	CD_3COCD_3 P, T	28
$C\mathbf{H}_3CD_3$	(y)	12.2	12.0	260–490	CD_3COCD_3 P	27, 39
$CH_3C\mathbf{D}_3$	(y)	14.1	12.1	260–490	CD_3COCD_3 P	27, 39

Metathetical Reactions of Methyl Radicals – Continued

Reactants	Notes	E	$\log_{10}A$	Temperature range	Radical source	References
		(*kcal mole*$^{-1}$)	(*cm*^{3} *mole*$^{-1}$ *sec*$^{-1}$)	°C		
$\mathbf{C_2D_6}$		14.8 ± 0.3	12.3	328–507	CH_3COCH_3 P, T	28
	(y)	13.6	12.3	260–490	CD_3COCD_3 P	27
C_3H_8	(g)		$k = 3.3 \times 10^9$	580	C_3H_8 T	29
		10.3	11.91	300–460	CD_3COCD_3 P	30
$C\mathbf{H}_3CD_2C\mathbf{H}_3$	(y)	**11.6**	12.08	300–450	CD_3COCD_3 P	31, 39
$CH_3C\mathbf{D}_2CH_3$	(y)	11.6	11.85	300–450	CD_3COCD_3 P	31, 39
n-C_4H_{10}		8.3 ± 0.2	11.0	122–198	CH_3COCH_3 P	19, 26
		8.2 ± 0.5	11.3	130–220	$Hg(CH_3)_2$ P	32
	(h)	9.5 ± 0.5	11.5		$Hg(CH_3)_2$ P	32
		8.6 ± 0.3	11.2	92–223	$Hg(CH_3)_2$ P	33
	(h)		$k = 1.3 \times 10^7$	182	$Hg(CH_3)_2$ P	34
		9.1 ± 0.3	11.4	79–162	$(CH_3)_2N_2$ P	35
		9.6	11.92	250–449	CD_3COCD_3 P	36
	(y) (f)	10.3 ± 0.2		500–560	CD_3CDO T	29
$C\mathbf{H}_3CD_2CD_2C\mathbf{H}_3$	(y)	11.7	12.09	356–450	CD_3COCD_3 P	36
$CH_3C\mathbf{D}_2C\mathbf{D}_2CH_3$	(y)	11.7	12.12	356–450	CD_3COCD_3 P	36
iso-C_4H_{10}		7.6 ± 0.2	11.0	76–194	CH_3COCH_3 P	19, 26
		7.4 ± 0.3	10.8	93–220	$Hg(CH_3)_2$ P	33
		6.6 ± 0.3	10.3	25–169	$(CH_3)_2N_2$ P	35
		7.7	10.3	111–146	D.T.B.P. T	37
	(y)		$k = 2.05 \times 10^7$	198	CD_3COCD_3 P	38
	(y) (f)	9.0 ± 0.6		500–560	CD_3CDO T	29
$(CH_3)_3C\mathbf{H}$	(y)	8.2	11.47	300–460	CD_3COCD_3 P	30
$(C\mathbf{H}_3)_3CD$	(y)	11.7	12.26	300–460	CD_3COCD_3 P	30, 39
$(CH_3)_3C\mathbf{D}$	(y)	9.8	11.57	300–460	CD_3COCD_3 P	30, 39
n-C_5H_{12}		8.1 ± 0.2	11.0	89–178	CH_3COCH_3 P	19, 26
			$k = 1.0 \times 10^9$	540	n-C_5H_{12} T	40
		9.9 ± 2.7		540–580	n-C_5H_{12} T	29
iso-$\mathbf{C_5H_{12}}$			$k = 0.9 \times 10^9$	540	iso-C_5H_{12} T	40
neo-C_5H_{12}		10.0 ± 0.3	11.3	138–292	CH_3COCH_3 P	19, 26
		10.4 ± 0.3	11.3	131–251	$Hg(CH_3)_2$ P	33
			$k = 0.2 \times 10^9$	540	neo-C_5H_{12} T	40
	(y) (f)	10.8 ± 0.2		500–560	CD_3CDO T	29
n-C_6H_{14}		8.1 ± 0.2	11.1	92–184	CH_3COCH_3 P	19, 26
$(CH_3)_2CHCH(CH_3)_2$		6.9 ± 0.2	10.8	27–190	CH_3COCH_3 P	19, 26
		6.8 ± 0.2	10.7	28–220	$Hg(CH_3)_2$ P	33
	(y) (f)	7.3 ± 0.8		500–560	CD_3CDO T	29
	(y)	7.8 ± 0.4	11.3	166–293	CD_3COCD_3 P	26
$(C_2H_5)_3CH$		6.8 ± 0.3	10.5	76–238	$Hg(CH_3)_2$ P	41
n-C_8H_{18}			$k = 1.6 \times 10^9$	500	n-C_8H_{18} T	40

Reactants	Notes	E	$\log_{10}A$	Temperature range	Radical source	References
		(*kcal mole*$^{-1}$)	(*cm*^{3} *mole*$^{-1}$ *sec*$^{-1}$)	°C		
$(CH_3)_3CCH_2CH(CH_3)_2$		$k=0.7\times10^9$		500	$(CH_3)_3CCH_2CH(CH_3)_2$ T	40
$(CH_3)_2CHCH(CH_3)CH(CH_3)_2$		$k=1.9\times10^9$		500	$(CH_3)_2CHCH(CH_3)CH(CH_3)_2$ T	40
	(y)	7.9 ± 0.4	11.3	141–332	CD_3COCD_3 P	26
$(CH_3)_3CC(CH_3)_3$	(y)	9.5 ± 0.4	11.3	162–322	CD_3COCD_3 P	26
Cyclo-alkanes						
cyclo-C_3H_6		10.2 ± 1.0	11.1	100–250	$Hg(CH_3)_2$ P	42
	(y)	10.3 ± 0.4	11.0	139–292	CD_3COCD_3 P	43
	(y)	12.9	12.18	248–404	CD_3COCD_3 P	44
cyclo-C_4H_8	(y)	9.3 ± 0.4	11.4	154–307	CD_3COCD_3 P	43
		10.1	12.18	262–402	CD_3COCD_3 P	45
cyclo-C_5H_{10}	(i)	$k=5.7\times10^7$		303	$Hg(CH_3)_2$ T	46
	(y)	8.3 ± 0.2	11.4	66–296	CD_3COCD_3 P	43
	(y)	9.1	12.24	250–402	CD_3COCD_3 P	44
	(y)	9.0	12.10	160–500	CD_3COCD_3 P	47
cyclo-C_6H_{12}		8.3 ± 0.2	11.3	65–189	CH_3COCH_3 P	43
		8.3 ± 0.3	11.2	81–220	$Hg(CH_3)_2$ P	33
	(y)	9.5	12.47	254–481	CD_3COCD_3 P	48
cyclo-C_7H_{14}	(y)	8.9	12.49			48
Alkenes						
$CH_2{:}CH_2$	(y)	10.0 ± 0.4	11.3	188–340	CD_3COCD_3 P	49
	(y) (f)	7.3 ± 1.0		500–560	CD_3CDO T	29
$CH_3CH{:}CH_2$		8.2	11.04	107–168	D.T.B.P	50
	(y)	7.7 ± 0.4	10.8	163–304	CD_3COCD_3 P	49
	(y) (f)	8.0 ± 0.3		500–560	CD_3CDO T	29, 51
$CH_3CH{:}CHCH_3$	(y)	7.7 ± 0.4	11.1	188–342	CD_3COCD_3 P	49
$CH_2{:}CHCH_2CH_3$	(y)	7.6 ± 0.4	11.2	189–340	CD_3COCD_3 P	49
$(CH_3)_2C{:}CH_2$	(y)	7.3 ± 0.4	10.9	168–304	CD_3COCD_3 P	49
$CH_3CH_2CH_2CH{:}CH_2$	(y)	7.6 ± 0.4	11.2	188–346	CD_3COCD_3 P	49
$(CH_3)_2CHCH{:}CH_2$	(y)	7.4 ± 0.4	11.3	189–346	CD_3COCD_3 P	49
$(CH_3)_2C{:}C(CH_3)_2$	(y)	7.8 ± 0.4	11.6	188–341	CD_3COCD_3 P	49
Alkynes						
HC⋮CH	(y)	14.0		200–500	CD_3COCD_3 P	52
DC⋮CD		18.4		200–500	CH_3COCH_3 P	52

247-168 O-67—4

Reactants	Notes	E	$\log_{10}A$	Temperature range	Radical source	References
		(kcal mole⁻¹)	*(cm³ mole⁻¹ sec⁻¹)*	°C		
$CH_3C\vdots CCH_3$	(y)	8.6 ± 0.4	11.6	213–346	CD_3COCD_3 P	43
$CH\vdots CCH_2CH_3$	(y)	9.1 ± 0.4	11.9	183–347	CD_3COCD_3 P	43
Aromatic hydrocarbons						
C_6H_6		$k = 4.48 \times 10^6$		209	D.T.B.P. T	53
	(y)	9.2 ± 0.4	10.4	183–327	CD_3COCD_3 P	43
$C_6H_5CH_3$	(h)	7 ± 2	10.0	103–249	$Hg(CH_3)_2$ P	54
		11.0 ± 2		130–230	D.T.B.P. P	55
		7.3 ± 0.3	11.2	149–250	$Hg(CH_3)_2$ P	33
	(j)	13.03 ± 0.27	12.92 ± 0.08	346–701		56, 57, 58
	(z)	7.4 ± 0.3	10.47	100–253	CH_3COCH_3 P	59
		9.2 ± 0.3	11.4	159–270	D.T.B.P. T	53
		$k = (4.0 \pm 0.8) \times 10^5$		60	$CH_3N_2CH_3$ P	60
	(y)	8.3 ± 0.3	11.0	120–334	CD_3COCD_3 P	43
$C_6\mathbf{H}_5CD_3$		$k = (2.3 \pm 0.4) \times 10^4$		60	$CH_3N_2CH_3$ P	60
		10.2	10.7	100–300		72
$\mathbf{C_6H_5CD_3}$		$k = (2.6 \pm 0.2) \times 10^4$		60	$CH_3N_2CH_3$ P	60
		11.3	11.8	102–284	CH_3COCH_3 P	72
$C_6D_5C\mathbf{H}_3$		$k = (3.8 \pm 0.8) \times 10^5$		60	$CH_3N_2CH_3$ P	60
		9.6	11.6	106–284	CH_3COCH_3 P	72
$C_6\mathbf{D}_5CH_3$		$k = (1.0 \pm 0.2) \times 10^4$		60	$CH_3N_2CH_3$ P	60
		$k = 5.1 \times 10^4$		182	CH_3COCH_3 P	72
$C_6D_5CD_3$		$k = (3.7 \pm 0.2) \times 10^4$		60	$CH_3N_2CH_3$ P	60
$C_6H_5C_2H_5$	(z)	7.0 ± 0.3	10.82	85–183	CH_3COCH_3 P	59
$C_6H_5CH(CH_3)_2$	(z)	6.4 ± 0.5	10.76	123–249	CH_3COCH_3 P	59
o-$C_6H_4(CH_3)_2$	(z)	7.8 ± 0.3	11.13	101–205	CH_3COCH_3 P	61
m-$C_6H_4(CH_3)_2$	(z)	8.5 ± 0.3	11.45	100–197	CH_3COCH_3 P	61
p-$C_6H_4(CH_3)_2$	(z)	7.4 ± 0.2	10.82	99–197	CH_3COCH_3 P	61
	(k)	$k = 3.1 \times 10^7$		484	p-$C_6H_4(CH_3)_2$ T	62
$C_6H_4(CH_3)_2$	(k) (l)	$k = 6.9 \times 10^9$		700	$C_6H_4(CH_3)_2$ T	63
Halogenated aromatics						
o-$CH_3C_6H_4F$	(z)	6.0 ± 0.4	9.76	330–460	CH_3COCH_3 P	64
m-$CH_3C_6H_4F$	(z)	7.1 ± 0.2	10.32	330–460	CH_3COCH_3 P	64
p-$CH_3C_6H_4F$	(z)	5.7 ± 0.4	9.60	330–460	CH_3COCH_3 P	64

Reactants	Notes	E	$\log_{10}A$	Temperature range	Radical source	References
		(*kcal mole*$^{-1}$)	(*cm*^{3} *mole*$^{-1}$ *sec*$^{-1}$)	°C		
Alcohols						
CH_3OH		8.2 ± 0.2	10.7	103–219	CH_3COCH_3 P	43
		8.2 ± 0.5	10.6	100–250	$Hg(CH_3)_2$ P	42
		8.7 ± 0.2	10.76 ± 0.07	133–199	CH_3COCH_3 P	65
	(y)	8.4 ± 0.1	10.68 ± 0.05	125–250	CD_3COCD_3 P	73
$C\mathbf{H}_3OH$	(m)	10.4	11.38	133–199	CH_3COCH_3 P	65
	(y) (m)	8.1	10.38	125–250	CD_3COCD_3 P	73
$CD_3\mathbf{OH}$		6.4 ± 0.7	9.25 ± 0.3	133–199	CH_3COCH_3 P	65
	(y)	9.0 ± 0.1	10.46 ± 0.03	125–245	CD_3COCD_3 P	73
$C\mathbf{D}_3OH$		11.7 ± 0.6	11.25 ± 0.28	133–199	CH_3COCH_3 P	65
	(y)	9.3 ± 0.1	10.18 ± 0.06	125–245	CD_3COCD_3 P	73
C_2H_5OH	(y)	8.7 ± 0.4	11.5	189–341	CD_3COCD_3 P	43
$(CH_3)_2CH(OH)$	(y)	7.3 ± 0.4	11.0	214–347	CD_3COCD_3 P	43
Thiols						
CH_3SH		$k = 1.8 \times 10^7$		30	CH_3COCH_3 P	66
$CD_3S\mathbf{H}$		4.1 ± 0.2	11.03 ± 0.15	130–200	CH_3COCH_3 P	74
$C\mathbf{D}_3SH$		8.3 ± 0.1	10.88 ± 0.05	130–200	CH_3COCH_3 P	74
C_2H_5SH		$k = 3.5 \times 10^7$		30	CH_3COCH_3 P	66
$(CH_3)_2CHSH$		$k = 4.1 \times 10^7$		30	CH_3COCH_3 P	66
$(CH_3)_3CSH$		$k = 5.9 \times 10^7$		30	CH_3COCH_3 P	66
Amines (primary)						
CH_3NH_2		7.6	10.9	125–157	D.T.B.P. T	67
		7.2 ± 0.2	10.59 ± 0.12		$CH_3N_2CH_3$ P	68
	(y)	8.4 ± 0.4	11.3	183–340	CD_3COCD_3 P	43
$C\mathbf{H}_3NH_2$	(m)	8.7 ± 0.7	10.99 ± 0.37	120–175	$CH_3N_2CH_3$ P	69, 68
$CH_3N\mathbf{H}_2$	(m)	5.7 ± 0.40	9.55 ± 0.22	120–175	$CH_3N_2CH_3$ P	69, 68
$C\mathbf{H}_3ND_2$		9.00 ± 0.20	11.15 ± 0.12	120–175	$CH_3N_2CH_3$ P	69, 68
$CH_3N\mathbf{D}_2$		7.00 ± 0.30	9.61 ± 0.16	120–175	$CH_3N_2CH_3$ P	69, 68
$CD_3N\mathbf{H}_2$		6.00 ± 0.50	9.77 ± 0.28	120–175	$CH_3N_2CH_3$ P	69, 68
$C\mathbf{D}_3NH_2$		10.10 ± 0.30	10.86 ± 0.16	120–175	$CH_3N_2CH_3$ P	69, 68
$C_2H_5NH_2$		7.1	11.2	125–157	D.T.B.P. T	67
		7.3 ± 0.3	10.89 ± 0.18	110–180	$CH_3N_2CH_3$ P	75
$C\mathbf{H}_3CH_2NH_2$		$k = 6.3 \times 10^5$		150	$CH_3N_2CH_3$ P	75

Reactants	Notes	E	$\log_{10}A$	Temperature range	Radical source	References
		(kcal mole^{-1})	*(cm^3 mole^{-1} sec^{-1})*	°C		
$CH_3\mathbf{CH_2}NH_2$		8.1	11.2	110–180	$CH_3N_2CH_3$ P	75
$CH_3CH_2\mathbf{NH_2}$		6.5	9.9	110–180	$CH_3N_2CH_3$ P	75
$CH_3CH_2\mathbf{ND_2}$		7.6 ± 0.4	10.04 ± 0.21	110–180	$CH_3N_2CH_3$ P	75
$\mathbf{CD_3}CH_2ND_2$		$k = 1.3 \times 10^5$		150	$CH_3N_2CH_3$ P	75
Amines (secondary)						
$(CH_3)_2NH$		7.2	11.7	125–157	D.T.B.P. P	67
		7.00 ± 0.30	11.20 ± 0.13	120–180	$CH_3N_2CH_3$ P	70
	(y)	7.2 ± 0.4	11.3	184–341	CD_3COCD_3 P	43
$(CH_3)_2N\mathbf{H}$		6.40 ± 0.30	10.81 ± 0.21	120–175	$CH_3N_2CH_3$ P	70
$(\mathbf{CH_3})_2ND$		8.70 ± 0.60	11.46 ± 0.28	120–175	$CH_3N_2CH_3$ P	70
$(CH_3)_2N\mathbf{D}$		7.80 ± 0.40	10.65 ± 0.22	120–175	$CH_3N_2CH_3$ P	70
$(C_2H_5)_2NH$		7.2	11.8	125–157	D.T.B.P. T	67
	(n)	5.7 ± 1.0	10.7	123–260	CH_3COCH_3 P	71
$((CH_3)_2CH)_2NH$		7.8	12.0	125–157	D.T.B.P. T	67
Amines (tertiary)						
$(CH_3)_3N$		8.0	11.4	132–269	CH_3COCH_3 P	71
		8.9 ± 0.1	11.9 ± 0.1	123–232	CH_3COCH_3 P	76
	(y)	8.8 ± 0.4	11.8	193–302	CD_3COCD_3 P	43
$(\mathbf{C_2H_5})_3N$	(n)	5.3 ± 1.0	10.4	123–260	CH_3COCH_3 P	71
Imines						
$(CH_2)_2NH$		4.8 ± 0.3	10.7	125–157	D.T.B.P. T	77
	(o)	5.28	10.76	100–216	CH_3COCH_3 P	78
		4.77 ± 0.44	10.29 ± 0.23	110–175	$CH_3N_2CH_3$ P	79, 80
	(y)	5.4	10.94	120–260	CD_3COCD_3 P	78
$(\mathbf{CH_2})_2NH$	(m)	10.10 ± 2.80	11.44 ± 1.48	110–175	$CH_3N_2CH_3$ P	79, 80
$(CH_2)_2N\mathbf{H}$		4.57 ± 0.10	10.17 ± 0.05	110–175	$CH_3N_2CH_3$ P	79, 80
$(CH_2)_2N\mathbf{D}$		6.34 ± 0.21	10.17 ± 0.13	110–175	$CH_3N_2CH_3$ P	79, 80
$(CH_2)_2NC(CH_3)_3$		6.6	9.6	125–157	D.T.B.P. T	67
$CH_3CH{:}NC(CH_3)_3$		7.8	11.1	125–157	D.T.B.P. T	67
Amides, azines, etc.						
$HCONH_2$		6.6	10.5	170–247	CH_3COCH_3 P	81
$HCONHCH_3$		7.6	10.9	161–287	CH_3COCH_3 P	81
$HCON(CH_3)_2$		8.3	11.4	120–298	CH_3COCH_3 P	81

Reactants	Notes	E	$\log_{10}A$	Temperature range	Radical source	References
		(*kcal mole*$^{-1}$)	(*cm*^{3} *mole*$^{-1}$ *sec*$^{-1}$)	°C		
CH_3CONH_2	(q)	9.2 ± 0.3	10.8	144–224	CH_3CONH_2 P	82
$CH_3CON(CH_3)_2$		8.3 ± 0.2	11.3 ± 0.1	106–232	CH_3COCH_3 P	76
$(CH_3)_2NCON(CH_3)_2$		7.3 ± 0.2	11.0 ± 0.1	108–235	CH_3COCH_3 P	76
CH_3ONH_2		4.53 ± 0.25	10.70 ± 0.15	70–190	$CH_3N_2CH_3$ P	83
$CH_3ON\mathbf{D}_2$		5.88 ± 0.22	10.55 ± 0.12	70–190	$CH_3N_2CH_3$ P	83
$(CH_3)_2N.NH_2$		5.80 ± 0.20	11.34 ± 0.12	110–180	$CH_3N_2CH_3$ P	68
$(C\mathbf{H}_3)_2N.NH_2$	(r)	8.5	11.6	110–180	$CH_3N_2CH_3$ P	68
$CH_3CH{:}NN{:}CHCH_3$		6.1	10.5	125–157	D.T.B.P. T	67
$CH_3N_2CH_3$		7.6 ± 0.3	11.1	60–182	$CH_3N_2CH_3$ P	84
		7.3	10.49	25–150	$CH_3N_2CH_3$ P	85
		6.86 ± 0.18	10.37	−47–50	$CH_3N_2CH_3$ P	86
		8.4 ± 0.3	11.40	80–180	$CH_3N_2CH_3$ P	87
	(s)	7.83 ± 0.08	10.97 ± 0.04	70–190	$CH_3N_2CH_3$ P	83
		8.7	11.47	50–180	$CH_3N_2CH_3$ P	89
$CH_3N{:}N(O)CH_3$		6 ± 2		27–121	$CH_3N{:}N(O)CH_3$ P	90
Aldehydes						
HCHO			$k=4.7\times10^7$	120	CH_3COCH_3/O_2 P	91
		6.2 ± 0.3	11.06	80–180	$CH_3N_2CH_3$ P	87
		6.6	11.25	111–146	D.T.B.P. T	37
DCDO		7.9 ± 0.3	11.15	80–180	$CH_3N_2CH_3$ P	87
CH_3CHO		7.9 ± 0.3	12.15	124–156	D.T.B.P. T	92
		6.8	11.5	91–165	$CH_3N_2CH_3$ P	93
		8.5	12.4	133–291	CH_3CHO P	94
		8.7		109–345	CH_3CHO P	95
		7.6 ± 0.2	11.9 ± 0.1	119–175	D.T.B.P. T	96
		6.8	11.50	25–250	$CH_3N_2CH_3$ P	97
	(y) (f)	6.5 ± 0.3		500–560	CD_3CDO T	29
CH_3CDO		7.9	11.8	27–158	$CH_3N_2CH_3$ P	93
C_2H_5CHO		7.5	11.9	122–156	D.T.B.P. T	99, 92
$CH_2{:}CHCH_2CHO$		10.9	13.3	119–175	D.T.B.P. T	96
n-C_3H_7CHO		7.3 ± 0.3	11.8 ± 0.2	119–175	D.T.B.P. T	96
n-C_3F_7CHO		5.55 ± 0.20	11.20	27–306	CH_3COCH_3/ C_3F_7CHO P	98
iso-C_3H_7CHO		8.7 ± 0.3	12.6 ± 0.2	119–175	D.T.B.P. T	96
n-C_4H_9CHO		8.0 ± 0.3	12.1 ± 0.2	119–175	D.T.B.P. T	96
iso-C_4H_9CHO		8.4 ± 0.3	12.3 ± 0.2	119–175	D.T.B.P. T	96

Metathetical Reactions of Methyl Radicals – Continued

Reactants	Notes	E	$\log_{10}A$	Temperature range	Radical source		References
		(*kcal mole*$^{-1}$)	(*cm*^{3} *mole*$^{-1}$ *sec*$^{-1}$)	°*C*			
sec-C_4H_9CHO		10.4 ± 0.3	13.1 ± 0.3	119–175	D.T.B.P.	T	96
t-C_4H_9CHO		10.2 ± 0.3	13.0 ± 0.3	119–175	D.T.B.P.	T	96
Ketones							
CH_3COCH_3	(t)	9.7 ± 0.1	11.6	121–300	CH_3COCH_3	P	100
	(h)	9.6 ± 0.4	11.5	100–250	CH_3COCH_3	P	101
		9.7 ± 0.2	11.8	125–220	CH_3COCH_3 and $Hg(CH_3)_2$	P	102
		9.8	11.59	271–439	CH_3COCH_3	P	103
		9.5 ± 1.5	11.5	127–175	D.T.B.P.	T	104
		9.5 ± 0.3	11.8	130–155	D.T.B.P.	T	105
		9.8 ± 0.4	11.60	27–412	CH_3COCH_3	P	13
		9.56	11.43	132–292	CH_3COCH_3	P	2, 15
$CD_3COCD_2\mathbf{H}$	(y) (u)	9.95 ± 0.15	10.74	120–250	CD_3COCD_3	P	73
	(y) (u)	9.48	9.87	125–200	CD_3COCD_3	P	74
CD_3COCD_3	(y)	10.3 ± 0.2	11.6	138–292	CD_3COCD_3	P	100
	(y)	10.6 ± 0.3	11.8	130–290	CD_3COCD_3	P	1
	(y)	11.6 ± 0.3	11.8	135–290	CD_3COCD_3	P	3
	(y)	11.6	12.07	150–250	CD_3COCD_3	P	30
	(y)	11.44 ± 0.05	11.66 ± 0.03	120–250	CD_3COCD_3	P	73
	(y)	11.29 ± 0.03	11.57 ± 0.01	125–200	CD_3COCD_3	P	74
	(y)	10.9 ± 1.0	11.5	130–200	CD_3COCD_3	P	110
CF_3COCH_3		8.9	12.0	25–113	CF_3COCH_3	P	109
$CH_3COC_2H_5$		7.4	10.6	79–190	$CH_3COC_2H_5$	P	166
$C_2H_5COC_2H_5$		8.0 ± 0.2	11.8	130–155	D.T.B.P.	T	105
		7.0 ± 0.1	11.2	26–134	$CH_3N_2CH_3$	P	85
	(y)	$k=2.9\times10^7$		141	CD_3COCD_3	P	111
cyclo-$C_3H_5COCH_3$		9.6 ± 1		60–170	cyclo-$C_3H_5COCH_3$	P	112
$C_6H_5COCH_3$		7.4	10.7	273–407	$C_6H_5COCH_3$	P	113
$CH_3COCOCH_3$		7.1 ± 0.2		28–200	$CH_3COCOCH_3$	P	114
		8.5	11.3	140–198	$CH_3N_2CH_3$	P	116
		7.7		28–200	$CH_3COCOCH_3$	P	115
Esters							
$HCOOCH_3$		9.0	10.9	77–230	CH_3COCH_3	P	117
		9.8	11.3				117
$HCOOC_2H_5$		8.2	10.5	77–230	CH_3COCH_3	P	117
$HCOOCH_2CH_2CH_3$		7.3	10.1	74–178	CH_3COCH_3	P	118
$HCOOCH(CH_3)_2$		8.9	10.9	94–181	CH_3COCH_3	P	118
$HCOOCH_2CH_2CH_2CH_3$		8.2	10.6	75–186	CH_3COCH_3	P	119

Metathetical Reactions of Methyl Radicals—Continued

Reactants	Notes	E	$\log_{10}A$	Temperature range	Radical source	References
		(*kcal mole*$^{-1}$)	(*cm*^{3} *mole*$^{-1}$ *sec*$^{-1}$)	°*C*		
CH_3COOCH_3		10 ± 0.5	11.2	63–216	CH_3COOCH_3 P	120
$C\mathbf{H}_3COOCD_3$		10 ± 0.5	11.4	151–340	CH_3COCH_3 P	121
		10 ± 0.5	11.4	145–350	CH_3COOCD_3 P	122
$CH_3COOC\mathbf{D}_3$		14 ± 1	11.8	151–274	CH_3COCH_3 P	121
$C_2H_5COOC_2H_5$		8.2	11.3	72–344	$C_2H_5COOC_2H_5$ P	123
$CH_3OCOOCH_3$		8.9 ± 0.7	10.29 ± 0.34	122–253	CH_3COCH_3 P	106
Acids and acid anhydrides						
$C\mathbf{H}_3COOD$		10.2	11.1	105–285	CH_3COOD P	124
$(CH_3CO)_2O$		9.6	11.3	107–196	$(CH_3CO)_2O$ P	125
Ethers and epoxides						
CH_3OCH_3		9.5 ± 0.2	11.5	108–198	CH_3COCH_3 P	43
		8.4 ± 1.5	11.0	100–250	$Hg(CH_3)_2$ P	42
		10 ± 2	11.8	199–292	$CH_3OCH_3 - H$	126
	(y) (f)	10.8 ± 1.0		500–560	CD_3CDO T	29
$(C_2H_5)_2O$		9.75 ± 0.5	12.14	145–179	D.T.B.P. T	127
$[(CH_3)_2CH]_2O$	(y)	7.3 ± 0.4	11.1	179–339	CD_3COCD_3 P	43
$\overset{\diagup O \diagdown}{CH_2-CH_2}$		9.6 ± 2	11.0	100–200	$Hg(CH_3)_2$ P	42
Peroxides						
CH_3OOCH_3		10.0	12.56	124–185	CH_3OOCH_3 T	128
$((CH_3)CHO)_2$			$k = 4.7 \times 10^5$	26	$((CH_3)_2CHO)_2$ P	129
			$k = 5.3 \times 10^6$	77	$((CH_3)_2CHO)_2$ P	129
$((CH_3)_3CO)_2$		11.7 ± 0.3	12.4	130–155	D.T.B.P. T	105
		14.5 ± 2.5		103–145	D.T.B.P. T	37
Nitriles						
CH_3CN	(y)	10.0 ± 0.5	11.5	100–290	CD_3COCD_3 P	130
C_2H_5CN	(y)	8.5 ± 0.5	11.5	133–297	CD_3COCD_3 P	130
Metal alkyls						
$Hg(CH_3)_2$	(h)	10.8	11.7	25–250	$Hg(CH_3)_2$ P	131
		9.0 ± 0.5	11.3	25–250	$Hg(CH_3)_2$ P	131
		10.8 ± 0.3	11.7	28–251	$Hg(CH_3)_2$ P	33
		10.2 ± 1.0	10.97	160–238	CH_3COCH_3 P	110
			$k = 4.8 \times 10^7$	407	$Hg(CH_3)_2$ T	132
	(y)	10.0 ± 1.0	11.22	125–202	CD_3COCD_3 P	110
$Cd(CH_3)_2$		14 ± 2	12.8	200–275	$Cd(CH_3)_2$ P	5

Metathetical Reactions of Methyl Radicals—Continued

Reactants	Notes	E	$\log_{10}A$	Temperature range	Radical source		References
		(kcal mole^{-1})	*(cm^3 mole^{-1} sec^{-1})*	°C			
Halogenated alkanes							
CFH_3	(v)	8.7 ± 0.3	11.6	125–211	CH_3COCH_3	P	133, 135
	(y)	11.8	11.2	193–331	CD_3COCD_3	P	134
CF_2H_2	(v)	6.2 ± 0.3	10.5	129–192	CH_3COCH_3	P	133, 135
	(y)	10.4	11.0	122–301	CD_3COCD_3	P	134
CF_3H	(y)	9.8	9.8	142–293	CD_3COCD_3	P	136, 137
		10.4	10.0	144–309	CD_3COCD_3	P	138
C_2F_5H	(y)	9.7	10.8	135–318	CD_3COCD_3	P	138
C_3F_7H	(y)	9.3	10.6	129–323	CD_3COCD_3	P	138
CH_3Cl	(v)	9.4 ± 0.3	11.8	127–207	CH_3COCH_3	P	133, 135
CH_2Cl_2	(v)	7.2 ± 0.3	11.3	129–211	CH_3COCH_3	P	133, 135
$CHCl_3$	(v)	5.8 ± 0.3	10.8	132–203	CH_3COCH_3	P	133, 135
		6.8		30	CH_3COCH_3	P	139
CH_3Br	(v)	10.1 ± 0.3	12.5	121–208	CH_3COCH_3	P	133, 135
CH_2Br_2	(v)	8.7 ± 0.3	12.2	126–177	CH_3COCH_3	P	133, 135
Hydrides of nitrogen, oxygen, and sulphur							
NH_3		9.8 ± 0.9	11.00 ± 0.42	110–180	$CH_3N_2CH_3$	P	88, 68
		10.0 ± 0.2	10.9 ± 0.1	144–308	CH_3COCH_3	P	76
	(y)	10.0 ± 0.4	10.8	180–339	CD_3COCD_3	P	43
ND_3		10.9 ± 0.9	11.00 ± 0.42	110–180	$CH_3N_2CH_3$	P	88, 68
N_2H_4		5.00 ± 0.1	11.00 ± 0.05	110–180	$CH_3N_2CH_3$	P	88, 68
H_2O	(b)	24.7	13.57				8
H_2S		2.6	11.4	50–140	CH_3COCH_3	P	140
	(w)	3.6	12.1	200–360	CH_3CHO	P	141
Hydrogen halides							
HCl		2.3 ± 1	11.6	28–150	CH_3COCH_3	P	142
	(e)	4.51	12.1				143, 144
HI	(x)	2.30	12.50	260–316	CH_3I/HI	T	145

FLUORINE ATOM TRANSFER

Reactants	Notes	E	$\log_{10}A$	Temperature range	Radical source		References
SF_6		14.1	13.3	157–168	D.T.B.P.	T	169

Metathetical Reactions of Methyl Radicals – Continued

Reactants	Notes	E	$\log_{10}A$	Temperature range	Radical source	References
		(*kcal mole*$^{-1}$)	(*cm*^{3} *mole*$^{-1}$ *sec*$^{-1}$)	°C		
CHLORINE ATOM TRANSFER						
CCl_4		12.9 ± 0.7	13.4	90–145	D.T.B.P. T	146, 147
CCl_3CN		10.4 ± 1.0	12.9	90–145	D.T.B.P. T	147
C_2Cl_6		10.1 ± 0.9	11.8	90–145	D.T.B.P. T	146, 147
$C_6H_5CCl_3$		7.6 ± 0.8	10.3	90–145	D.T.B.P. T	147
CCl_3COCCl_3		9.7 ± 0.8	12.6	90–145	D.T.B.P. T	146, 147
BROMINE ATOM TRANSFER						
CF_3Br		12.5 ± 1.0	13.3	90–145	D.T.B.P. T	147
CF_2Br_2		6.4 ± 1.0	11.0	90–145	D.T.B.P. T	147
CCl_3Br		7.1 ± 0.9	13.2	90–145	D.T.B.P. T	147
CCl_2Br_2		7.6 ± 1.1	13.8	90–145	D.T.B.P. T	147
CBr_4		7.9 ± 1.1	14.2	90–145	D.T.B.P. T	147
IODINE ATOM TRANSFER						
I_2			$k=2\times10^{12}-2\times10^{13}$	20	CH_3I/O_2 P	148
			$k=2.0\times10^{16}$	50	CH_3I P	149
	(aa)	1.50	13.0	260–316	CH_3I/HI T	145
			$k=1.1\times10^{13}$	60	CH_3I F.P.	165
CF_3I		7.5 ± 1.0	13.8	90–145	D.T.B.P. T	147
OXYGEN ATOM TRANSFER						
O_2	(bb)		$k=5.3\times10^8$	498	CH_3COCH_3/O_2 T	150
NO_2		5.7	12.75	1150–1590	CH_3NO_2 ignition	151
GROUP-TRANSFER REACTIONS						
$^{14}CH_3+CH_3COCH_3 = {}^{14}CH_3COCH_3 + CH_3$	(ee)		$k=5.2\times10^6$	350	CH_3COCH_3 P	16
$CH_3+CF_3COCF_3 = CH_3COCF_3+CF_3$		5.7 ± 1.5	9.3	163–245	$CH_3N_2CH_3$ P, T	171
		6.2 ± 1.0	11.4	85–210	CF_3COCF_3 P	172
		7.0 ± 1.0	11.7	48–240	CH_3COCH_3/CF_3COCF_3 P	173

Metathetical Reactions of Methyl Radicals—Continued

Reactants	Notes	E	$\log_{10}A$	Temperature range	Radical source		Reference
		(*kcal mole*$^{-1}$)	(*cm*^{3} *mole*$^{-1}$ *sec*$^{-1}$)	°C			
$CH_3 + C_2F_5COC_2F_5 = CH_3COC_2F_5 + C_2F_5$		7 ± 1		184–240	$(C_2F_5)_2CO$	P	174
$CD_3 + CH_3HgCH_3 = CD_3HgCH_3 + CH_3$			$k = 8.9 \times 10^5$	180	CD_3COCD_3	P	175, 176
$CH_3 + CD_3SH = CH_3SH + CD_3$		7.6	10.73	130–200	CH_3COCH_3	P	74
$CH_3 + CF_3COCH_3 = C_2H_6 + CF_3CO$		14		150–350	CF_3COCH_3	P	109
$CH_3 + CH_3COCOCH_3 = CH_3COCH_3 + CH_3CO$		5.6	10.7	100–200	$CH_3COCOCH_3$	P	114
		6.6		100–200	$CH_3COCOCH_3$	P	115
$CH_3 + CH_3CH{:}CHCHO = CH_3CH{:}CHCH_3 + CHO$		7.45 ± 1.30	11.8 ± 0.4	120–250	CH_3COCH_3	P	177
$CH_3 + CH_3HgCH_3 = C_2H_6 + (Hg + CH_3)$		1.0	7	175–220	CH_3HgCH_3	P	131, 178

Ratios of Rate Constants (Methyl Radicals)

(i) Reactions with halogens and hydrogen halides.

Reaction	Notes	$E_1 - E_2$	$\log_{10}A_1/A_2$	k_1/k_2	Temperature range	Radical source		Reference
		(*kcal mole*$^{-1}$)			°C			
(1) $CH_3 + HBr = CH_4 + Br$ (2) $CH_3 + Br_2 = CH_3Br + Br$		2.0	−0.7		37–210	$CH_4/Br/HBr$	P	167, 168
(1) $CH_3 + HI = CH_4 + I$ (2) $CH_3 + I_2 = CH_3I + I$				0.15	280	CH_3I/HI	T	152, 154
				0.13 ± 0.03	270–310	CH_3I/HI	T	153, 154
		1.3 ± 0.5	−0.38		126–295	CH_3COCH_3	P	155
		0.8 ± 1.0	−0.50 ± 0.40		260–316	CH_3I/HI	T	145
		0.75	−0.64		83–192	CH_3I/HI	P	164
(1) $CH_3 + HBr = CH_4 + Br$ (2) $CH_3 + I_2 = CH_3I + I$		0.8 ± 0.3			60	$CH_3I/HBr/I_2$	P	163
		1.37 ± 0.26	−0.30 ± 0.13		80–164	CH_3COCH_3	P	156
		0.95	−0.88		83–192	CH_3I/HBr	P	164
(1) $CH_3 + HBr = CH_4 + Br$ (2) $CH_3 + HI = CH_4 + I$	(cc)	1.1 ± 0.4		0.15	25	CH_3I/HBr	P	157

Ratios of Rate Constants (Methyl Radicals)—Continued

(i) Reactions with halogens and hydrogen halides.—Continued

Reaction	Notes	E_1-E_2	$\log_{10}A_1/A_2$	k_1/k_2	Temperature range	Radical source	Reference
		(*kcal mole*$^{-1}$)			°C		
(1) $CH_3+CH_3I=CH_4+CH_2I$ (2) $CH_3+HI=CH_4+I$				0.03	270–310	CH_3I/HI T	153, 154
(1) $CH_3+HCl=CH_4+Cl$ (2) $CH_3+I_2=CH_3I+I$	(dd)	2.4	−1.46		98–160	CH_3I/HCl P	164
(1) $CH_3+I_2=CH_3I+I$ (2) $CH_3+NO=CH_3NO$				6	25	CH_3I/NO P	158
(1) $CH_3+CH_4=CH_4+CH_3$ (2) $CH_3+I_2=CH_3I+I$		6.5±2	−3.8		30–252	$CH_3I/CH_4/I_2$ P	161

(ii) Miscellaneous reactions.

Reaction	Notes	E_1-E_2	$\log_{10}A_1/A_2$	k_1/k_2	Temperature range	Radical source	Reference
		(*kcal mole*$^{-1}$)			°C		
(1) $CH_3+CH_3CD_3=CH_3D+CH_3CD_2$ (2) $CH_3+CH_3CD_3=CH_4+CH_2CD_3$		0.6±0.04	−0.32		328–424	$CH_3N_2CH_3$ T	159, 27
(1) $CH_3+CH_3CD_2CH_3=CH_3D+CH_3CDCH_3$ (2) $CH_3+CH_3CD_2CH_3=CH_4+CH_2CD_2CH_3$		−1.7	−0.66		312–421	$CH_3N_2CH_3$ T	159, 27
(1) $CH_3+(CH_3)_3CD=CH_3D+(CH_3)_3C$ (2) $CH_3+(CH_3)_3CD=CH_4+CH_2(CH_3)_2CD$		−2.3	−0.51		305–359	$CH_3N_2CH_3$ T	159, 27
(1) $CD_3+CD_3COCD_2CH_2CH_3=CD_4+[C_5D_4H_5O]$ (2) $CD_3+CD_3COCD_2CH_2CH_3=CD_3H+[C_5D_5H_4O]$		0.7			35–144	$CD_3COCD_2CH_2CH_3$ P, T	36
(1) $CH_3+CH_3OCH_2CH_3=CH_4+[C_3H_7O]$ (2) $CH_3+CH_3OCH_3=CH_4+CH_2OCH_3$				4 to 12	525	CH_3OCH_3 T	160
(1) $CH_3+HCHO=CH_4+HCO$ (2) $CH_3+CH_3OCH_3=CH_4+CH_2OCH_3$				3	507	CH_3OCH_3 T	9
(1) $CH_3+O_2=HCHO+OH$ (2) $CH_3+O_2+M=CH_3O_2+M$				1.0×10^{-8} k_1/k_2 [M] $=0.49$	25 162	CH_3I/O_2 P $CH_3N_2CH_3/O_2$ P	170 162

Notes

(a) When corrected, these activation energies are 10.5 and 12.2 kcal respectively (see ref. 11).

(b) This value was used (without a source being quoted), in the range 1000–1500 °C.

(c) Use of the more recent activation energy for CH_3+CH_3CHO gives $E=12.0$ kcal (see ref. 11).

(d) For a re-analysis of these results see reference 15.

(e) Calculated from the reverse reaction.

(f) Assuming an activation energy of 9.2 kcal/mole for the reaction $CD_3+CD_3CDO=CD_4+CD_3CO$.

(g) Assuming $k=10^{12.3}$ exp $(-13{,}600/RT)$ for the reaction $CH_3+C_2D_6=CH_3D+C_2D_5$.

(h) The quantities were not calculated in this manner by the original authors.

(i) Assuming $k=10^{11.7}$ exp $(-10{,}800/RT)$ for the reaction $CH_3+CH_3HgCH_3=CH_4+CH_2HgCH_3$.

(j) Pyrolysis of a series of methyl metal derivatives.

(k) Assuming $k=10^{11.8}$ exp $(-12{,}000/RT)$ for the reaction $CH_3+D_2=CH_3D+D$.

(l) No distinction made between *o*, *m*, and *p* xylenes.

(m) Calculated assuming a zero secondary isotope effect.

(n) These are not the values quoted by the authors, but corrected (see ref. 67) for arithmetical errors.

(o) No significant quantities of CH_3D were formed, when acetone was photolyzed in presence of $(CD_2)_2NH$.

(p) These values are doubtful.

(q) No significant quantities of CH_3D formed during the photolysis of CH_3COND_2.

(r) Calculated assuming the parameters for abstraction from the $-NH_2$ group, are as for those in hydrazine.

(s) See also references 69, 70, 75, 79, 80, and 88.

(t) Several other studies are in excellent agreement with those listed. See references 1, 23, 59, 65, 74, 106, 107, and 108.

(u) "A" factor doubtful.

(v) The results for CCl_4, CH_2Cl_2, and CH_3Cl are invalid: the others are to be regarded with some suspicion (see ref. 135).

(w) Assuming $k=10^{11.9}$ exp $(-7600/RT)$ for the reaction $CH_3+CH_3CHO=CH_4+CH_3CO$.

(x) The authors consider the activation energy to be ~ 1 kcal too high.

(y) The attacking radical is CD_3.

(z) The variations reported within these series may be spurious as variations in *E* are compensated by variations in *A*.

(aa) The authors consider the activation energy to be ~ 1 kcal too high.

(bb) The products of this reaction are HCHO and OH.

(cc) Activation energy difference calculated assuming identical *A* factors.

(dd) "Hot" methyl radicals may have played an important part in this system.

(ee) Assuming $k=10^{11.6}$ exp $(-9800/RT)$ for the reaction $CH_3+CH_3COCH_3=CH_4+CH_2COCH_3$.

References (Methyl Radical Reactions)

1. Majury and Steacie, Disc. Faraday Soc. **14,** 45 (1953).
2. Majury and Steacie, Can. J. Chem. **30,** 800 (1952).
3. Whittle and Steacie, J. Chem. Phys. **21,** 993 (1953).
4. Phibbs and Darwent, Trans. Faraday Soc. **45,** 541 (1949).
5. Anderson and Taylor, J. Phys. Chem. **56,** 498 (1952).
6. Davison and Burton, J. Am. Chem. Soc. **74,** 2307 (1952).
7. Gesser and Steacie, Can. J. Chem. **34,** 113 (1956).
8. Intezarova, Kondratiev, and Mukhoyan. Kinetika i Kataliz, **5,** 585 (1964).
9. Benson and Jain, J. Chem. Phys. **31,** 1008 (1959).
10. Skinner and Ringrose, J. Chem. Phys. **43,** 4129 (1965).
11. Wijnen and Steacie, Disc. Faraday Soc. **14,** 118 (1953).
12. Rebbert and Steacie, Can. J. Chem. **32,** 113 (1954).
13. Chanmugam and Burton, J. Am. Chem. Soc. **78,** 509 (1956).
14. McNesby, Gordon, and Smith, J. Am. Chem. Soc. **78,** 1287 (1956).
15. Pritchard and Pritchard, Can. J. Chem. **41,** 3042 (1963).
16. Dainton, Ivin, and Wilkinson, Trans. Faraday Soc. **55,** 929 (1959).
17. Creak, Dainton, and Ivin, Trans. Faraday Soc. **58,** 326 (1962).
18. Trotman-Dickenson, "Gas Kinetics," p. 199 (Butterworths, 1955).
19. Trotman-Dickenson and Steacie, J. Phys. Chem. **55,** 908 (1951).
20. McNesby and Gordon, J. Am. Chem. Soc. **76,** 4196 (1954).
21. Wijnen, J. Chem. Phys. **23,** 1357 (1955).
22. Dainton, Ivin, and Wilkinson, Trans. Faraday Soc. **53,** 1204 (1957).
23. Dainton and McElcheran, Trans. Faraday Soc. **51,** 657 (1955).
24. Brodskii, Kalinenko, and Lavrovskii, J. Chem. Soc. 4443 (1960).
25. Blackmore and Hinshelwood, Proc. Roy. Soc. **271A,** 34 (1963).
26. Trotman-Dickenson, Birchard, and Steacie, J. Chem. Phys. **19,** 163 (1951).
27. McNesby, J. Phys. Chem. **64,** 1671 (1960).
28. McNesby and Gordon, J. Am. Chem. Soc. **77,** 4719 (1955).
29. Rice and Varnerin, J. Am. Chem. Soc. **77,** 221 (1955).
30. Jackson, McNesby, and Darwent, J. Chem. Phys. **37,** 1610 (1962).
31. Jackson and McNesby, J. Am. Chem. Soc. **83,** 4891 (1961).
32. Gomer, J. Am. Chem. Soc. **72,** 201 (1950).
33. Rebbert and Steacie, J. Chem. Phys. **21,** 1723 (1953).
34. Smith and Taylor, J. Chem. Phys. **7,** 390 (1939).
35. Jones and Steacie, Can. J. Chem. **31,** 505 (1953).
36. McNesby and Gordon, J. Am. Chem. Soc. **78,** 3570 (1956).
37. Blake and Kutschke, Can. J. Chem. **37,** 1462 (1959).
38. Blake, Henderson, and Kutschke, Can. J. Chem. **39,** 1920 (1961).
39. Rice and Vanderslice, J. Am. Chem. Soc. **80,** 291 (1958).
40. Blackmore and Hinshelwood, Proc. Roy. Soc. **268A,** 36 (1962).
41. Rebbert and Steacie, Can. J. Chem. **32,** 40 (1954).
42. Phibbs and Darwent, Can. J. Res. **28B,** 395 (1950).
43. Trotman-Dickenson and Steacie, J. Chem. Phys. **19,** 329 (1951).
44. McNesby and Gordon, J. Am. Chem. Soc. **79,** 825 (1957).
45. Gordon, Smith, and Drew, J. Chem. Phys. **36,** 824 (1962).
46. Russell and Bernstein, J. Chem. Phys. **30,** 607 (1959).
47. Gordon, Can. J. Chem. **43,** 570 (1965).
48. Gordon and Smith, J. Phys. Chem. **66,** 521 (1962).
49. Trotman-Dickenson and Steacie, J. Chem. Phys. **19,** 169 (1951).
50. Miyoshi and Brinton, J. Chem. Phys. 36, 3019 (1962).
51. Rice and Varnerin, J. Am. Chem. Soc. **76,** 2629 (1954).
52. Drew and Gordon, J. Chem. Phys. **31,** 1417 (1959).
53. Mulcahy, Williams, and Wilmhurst, Austral. J. Chem. **17,** 1329 (1964).
54. Taylor and Smith, J. Chem. Phys. **8,** 543 (1940).
55. Szwarc and Roberts, Trans. Faraday Soc. **46,** 625 (1950).
56. Price and Trotman-Dickenson, J. Chem. Soc. 4205 (1958).
57. Price and Trotman-Dickenson, Trans. Faraday Soc. **53,** 939 (1957).
58. Price and Trotman-Dickenson, Trans. Faraday Soc. **53,** 1208 (1957).
59. Burkley and Rebbert, J. Phys. Chem. **67,** 168 (1963).
60. Cher, J. Phys. Chem. **68,** 1316 (1964).
61. Sanders and Rebbert, J. Phys. Chem. **67,** 170 (1963).
62. Burr and Strong, J. Chem. Phys. **43,** 1432 (1965).
63. Burr and Strong, J. Am. Chem. Soc. **86,** 5065 (1964).
64. Wunderlich and Rebbert, J. Phys. Chem. **67,** 1382 (1963).
65. Harrison and Shannon, Can. J. Chem. **41,** 2455 (1963).
66. Kerr and Trotman-Dickenson, J. Chem. Soc. 3322 (1957).

67. Brinton, Can. J. Chem. **38,** 1339 (1960).
68. Gray and Thynne, 10th Int. Comb. Symp., p. 435, Comb. Inst., Pittsburgh (1965).
69. Gray and Thynne, Trans. Faraday Soc. **59,** 2275 (1963).
70. Gray, Jones, and Thynne, Trans. Faraday Soc. **61,** 474 (1965).
71. Kozak and Gesser, J. Chem. Soc. 448 (1960).
72. Cher, Hollingsworth, and Sicilio, J. Phys. Chem. **70,** 877 (1966).
73. Shaw and Thynne, Trans. Faraday Soc. **62,** 104 (1966).
74. Greig and Thynne, Trans. Faraday Soc. **62,** 379 (1966).
75. Gray and Jones, Trans. Faraday Soc. **62,** 112 (1966).
76. Edwards, Kerr, Lloyd, and Trotman-Dickenson, J. Chem. Soc. 621 (1966).
77. Brinton and Volman, J. Chem. Phys. **20,** 25 (1952).
78. Klemm, Can. J. Chem. **43,** 2633 (1965).
79. Gray and Jones, Trans. Faraday Soc. **61,** 2161 (1965).
80. Gray and Jones, Can. J. Chem. **43,** 3485 (1965).
81. Cafferata, Kerr, and Trotman-Dickenson, J. Chem. Soc. 1386 (1965).
82. Spall and Steacie, Proc. Roy. Soc. **239A,** 1 (1957).
83. Thynne, Trans. Faraday Soc. **60,** 2207 (1964).
84. Jones and Steacie, J. Chem. Phys. **21,** 1018 (1953).
85. Ausloos and Steacie, Can. J. Chem. **32,** 593 (1954).
86. Toby, J. Am. Chem. Soc. **82,** 3822 (1960).
87. Toby and Kutschke, Can. J. Chem. **37,** 672 (1959).
88. Gray and Thynne, Trans. Faraday Soc. **60,** 1047 (1964).
89. Toby and Nimoy, J. Phys. Chem. **70,** 867 (1966).
90. Gowenlock, Can. J. Chem. **42,** 1936 (1964).
91. Hoare, Trans. Faraday Soc. **49,** 1292 (1953).
92. Brinton and Volman. J. Chem. Phys. **20,** 1053 (1952).
93. Ausloos and Steacie, Can. J. Chem. **33,** 31 (1955).
94. Dodd, Can. J. Chem. **33,** 699 (1955).
95. Calvert, Pitts, and Thompson, J. Am. Chem. Soc. **78,** 4239 (1956).
96. Birrell and Trotman-Dickenson, J. Chem. Soc. 2059 (1960).
97. Kerr and Calvert, J. Phys. Chem. **69,** 1022 (1965).
98. Pritchard, Hsia, and Miller, J. Am. Chem. Soc. **85,** 1568 (1963).
99. Volman and Brinton, J. Chem. Phys. **22,** 929 (1954).
100. Trotman-Dickenson and Steacie, J. Chem. Phys. **18,** 1097 (1950).
101. Saunders and Taylor, J. Chem. Phys. **9,** 616 (1941).
102. Gomer and Kistiakowsky, J. Chem. Phys. **19,** 85 (1951).
103. Mandelcorn and Steacie, Can. J. Chem. **32,** 331 (1954).
104. Jacquiss, Roberts, and Szwarc, J. Am. Chem. Soc. **74,** 6005 (1952).
105. Pritchard, Pritchard, and Trotman-Dickenson, J. Chem. Soc. 1425 (1954).
106. Thynne and Gray, Trans. Faraday Soc. **58,** 2403 (1962).
107. March and Polanyi, Proc. Roy. Soc. **273A,** 360 (1963).
108. Brinton, J. Am. Chem. Soc. **83,** 1541 (1961).
109. Sieger and Calvert, J. Am. Chem. Soc. **76,** 5197 (1954).
110. Oswin, Rebbert, and Steacie, Can. J. Chem. **33,** 472 (1955).
111. Wijnen, J. Chem. Phys. **22,** 1631 (1954).
112. Pitts and Norman, J. Am. Chem. Soc. **76,** 4815 (1954).
113. Duncan and Trotman-Dickenson, J. Chem. Soc. 4672 (1962).
114. Blacet and Bell, Disc. Faraday Soc. **14,** 70 (1953).
115. Bell and Blacet, J. Am. Chem. Soc. **76,** 5332 (1954).
116. Ausloos and Steacie, Can. J. Chem. **33,** 39 (1955).
117. Thynne, Trans. Faraday Soc. **58,** 676 (1962).
118. Thynne, Trans. Faraday Soc. **58,** 1394 (1962).
119. Thynne, Trans. Faraday Soc. **58,** 1533 (1962).
120. Wijnen, J. Chem. Phys. **27,** 710 (1957).
121. Wijnen, Can. J. Chem. **36,** 176 (1958).
122. Wijnen, J. Chem. Phys. **28,** 939 (1958).
123. Wijnen, J. Am. Chem. Soc. **80,** 2394 (1958).
124. Ausloos and Steacie, Can. J. Chem. **33,** 1530 (1955).
125. Ausloos, Can. J. Chem. **34,** 1709 (1956).
126. Marcus, Darwent, and Steacie, J. Chem. Phys. **16,** 987 (1948).
127. Long and Skirrow, Trans. Faraday Soc. **58,** 1403 (1962).
128. Thynne and Gray, Trans. Faraday Soc. **59,** 1149 (1963).
129. McMillan, J. Am. Chem. Soc. **83,** 3018 (1961).
130. Wijnen, J. Chem. Phys. **22,** 1074 (1954).
131. Gomer and Noyes, J. Am. Chem. Soc. **71,** 3390 (1949).
132. Kallend and Purnell, Trans. Faraday Soc. **60,** 103 (1964).
133. Raal and Steacie, J. Chem. Phys. **20,** 578 (1952).
134. Pritchard, Bryant, and Thommarson, J. Phys. Chem. **69,** 664 (1965).
135. Ridge and Steacie, Can. J. Chem. **33,** 396 (1955).
136. Pritchard, Pritchard, Schiff, and Trotman-Dickenson, Trans. Faraday Soc. **52,** 849 (1956).
137. Pritchard, Pritchard, Schiff, and Trotman-Dickenson, Chem. and Ind. 896 (1955).
138. Pritchard and Thommarson, J. Phys. Chem. **68,** 568 (1964).
139. Cvetanovic, Raal, and Steacie, Can. J. Chem. **31,** 171 (1953).
140. Imai and Toyama, Bull. Chem. Soc. Japan **33,** 652 (1960).
141. Imai and Toyama, Bull. Chem. Soc. Japan. **33,** 1120 (1960).
142. Cvetanovic and Steacie, Can. J. Chem. **31,** 158 (1953).
143. Pritchard, Pyke, and Trotman-Dickenson, J. Am. Chem. Soc. **77,** 2629 (1955).
144. Pritchard, Pyke, and Trotman-Dickenson, J. Am. Chem. Soc. **76,** 1201 (1954).
145. Flowers and Benson, J. Chem. Phys. **38,** 882 (1963).
146. Tomkinson, Galvin, and Pritchard, J. Phys. Chem. **68,** 541 (1964).
147. Tomkinson and Pritchard, J. Phys. Chem. **70,** 1579 (1966).
148. Christie, Proc. Roy. Soc. **244A,** 411 (1958).
149. Souffie, Williams, and Hamill, J. Am. Chem. Soc. **78,** 917 (1956).
150. Barnard and Honeyman, Proc. Roy. Soc. **279A,** 244 (1964).
151. Hiraoka and Hardwick, J. Chem. Phys. **39,** 2361 (1963).
152. Benson and O'Neal, J. Chem. Phys. **34,** 514 (1961).
153. Sullivan, J. Phys. Chem. **65,** 722 (1961).
154. Ogg, J. Am. Chem. Soc. **56,** 526 (1934).
155. O'Neal and Benson, J. Chem. Phys. **36,** 2196 (1962).
156. Fettis and Trotman-Dickenson, J. Chem. Soc. 3037 (1961).
157. Farren, Gilbert, Linnett and Read, Trans. Faraday Soc. **60,** 740 (1964).
158. Christie and Frost, Trans. Faraday Soc. **61,** 468 (1965).
159. Rice and Vanderslice, J. Am. Chem. Soc. **80,** 291 (1958).
160. Anderson and Benson, J. Chem. Phys. **36,** 2320 (1962).
161. Willard and Harris, J. Am. Chem. Soc. **76,** 4678 (1954).
162. Wenger and Kutschke, Can. J. Chem. **37,** 1546 (1959).
163. Anderson and Kistiakowsky, J. Chem. Phys. **11,** 6 (1943).
164. Williams and Ogg, J. Chem. Phys. **15,** 696 (1947).
165. Davidson and Carrington, J. Am. Chem. Soc. **74,** 6277 (1952).
166. Ausloos and Steacie, Can. J. Chem. **33,** 1062 (1955).
167. Kistiakowsky and Van Artsdalen, J. Chem. Phys. **12,** 469 (1944).
168. Benson and Buss, J. Chem. Phys. **28,** 301 (1958).
169. Batt and Cruickshank, J. Phys. Chem. **70,** 723 (1966).
170. Heicklen and Johnston, J. Am. Chem. Soc. **84,** 4030 (1962).
171. Pritchard and Steacie, Can. J. Chem. **35,** 1216 (1957).
172. Alcock and Whittle, Trans. Faraday Soc. **61,** 244 (1965).
173. Giles and Whittle, Trans. Faraday Soc. **61,** 1425 (1965).
174. Price and Kutschke, Can. J. Chem. **38,** 2128 (1960).
175. Rebbert and Ausloos, J. Am. Chem. Soc. **86,** 2068 (1964).
176. Rebbert and Ausloos, J. Am. Chem. Soc. **85,** 3086 (1963).
177. Allen and Pitts, J. Phys. Chem. **70,** 169 (1966).
178. Trotman-Dickenson, "Gas Kinetics," p. 237 et seq. (Butterworths, London, 1955).

Difluoromethylene Radicals

Reaction	Notes	E	$\log_{10}A$	Temperature range	Radical source	Reference
		(kcal mole⁻¹)	*(cm³ mole⁻¹ sec⁻¹)*	°C		
$CF_2 + O_2 = CO + 2F + O$		14.98	12.30	1307–2117	C_2F_4/O_2 S.T.	1

References

1. Modica and La Graff, J. Chem. Phys. **43,** 3383 (1965).

Trifluoromethyl Radicals

Reactants	Notes	E	$\log_{10}A$	Temperature range	Radical source	Reference
HYDROGEN ATOM TRANSFER						
Hydrogen		(*kcal mole*$^{-1}$)	(*mole*$^{-1}$ *cc. sec*$^{-1}$)	°C		
H_2		9.5 ± 0.7	11.86	59–158	CF_3COCF_3	1
		8.8	11.60	219–346	$CF_3N_2CF_3$	2
	(a)	25.1	11.89	832–1011		3
$\mathbf{H}D$		10.5 ± 1.5	11.78	102–174	CF_3COCF_3	1
$H\mathbf{D}$		10.2 ± 1.5	11.35	102–174	CF_3COCF_3	1
D_2		10.2 ± 0.7	11.45	86–196	CF_3COCF_3	1
		9.7	11.44	220–346	$CF_3N_2CF_3$	2
Alkanes						
CH_4		10.3 ± 0.5	11.70	122–251	CF_3COCF_3	4
		10.6	11.73	170–310	CF_3CHO	5
		9.5 ± 2	11.2	30–350	CF_3COCF_3	6
		11.0 ± 0.1	11.98	84–261	CF_3COCF_3	7
		11.3 ± 0.5	11.96 ± 0.22	153–295	CF_3COCF_3	8
		11.0	11.98			
$C\mathbf{H}D_3$		10.5 ± 0.3	11.04	55–354	CF_3COCF_3	9
$CH\mathbf{D}_3$		12.75 ± 0.3	11.33	55–354	CF_3COCF_3	9
CD_4		12.1 ± 2.1	11.18	106–287	CF_3COCF_3	7
C_2H_6		7.5 ± 0.5	11.68	81–216	CF_3COCF_3	4
		7.5	11.63	220–350	$CF_3N_2CF_3$	2
C_3H_8		6.2	11.67	200–310	$CF_3N_2CF_3$	2
		6.5 ± 0.5	11.75	27–119	CF_3COCF_3	10
n-C_4H_{10}		5.1 ± 0.3	11.15	29–93	CF_3COCF_3	10
		5.5 ± 1.0	10.9	30–350	CF_3COCF_3	6
		5.3	11.46	200–310	$CF_3N_2CF_3$	2
iso-C_4H_{10}		4.7 ± 0.3	11.15	28–84	CF_3COCF_3	10
		4.7	11.17	170–240	CF_3CHO	5
$(CH_3)_3C\mathbf{D}$		7.4 ± 1.0	12.48	62–208	CF_3COCF_3	7
neo-C_5H_{12}		7.6	11.76	250–320	$CF_3N_2CF_3$	2
$CH_3C(CH_3)_2CH_2CH_3$		1.7	10.22	250–300	$CF_3N_2CF_3$	2
Cyclo-Alkanes						
cyclo-C_5H_{10}		4.7	11.54	210–300	$CF_3N_2CF_3$	2
cyclo-C_6H_{12}		5.0 ± 0.2	11.44	19–91	CF_3COCF_3	11

Reactants	Notes	E	$\log_{10}A$	Temperature range	Radical source	Reference
		(kcal mole⁻¹)	*(mole⁻¹ cc. sec⁻¹)*	°C		
Aromatic hydrocarbons						
C_6H_6		6.3 ± 0.20	11.35	23–86	CF_3COCF_3	11
	(b)	7.7	11.44		$CF_3N_2CF_3$	2
$C_6H_5CH_3$	(b)	6.0	11.33		$CF_3N_2CF_3$	2
		5.91 ± 0.30	11.59 ± 0.20	27–110	CF_3COCF_3	12
		5.37 ± 0.26	11.10	25–81	CF_3COCF_3	11
$C_6H_5C\mathbf{D}_3$		5.8 ± 0.4	10.13	22–72	CF_3COCF_3	13
o-$C_6H_4(CH_3)_2$		5.55 ± 0.54	11.68	37–68	CF_3COCF_3	11
Halogenated Aromatics						
C_6H_5Cl		5.5 ± 0.3	10.56	20–118	CF_3COCF_3	14
C_6H_5Br		5.9 ± 0.5	11.53	23–95	CF_3COCF_3	14
C_6H_5I		4.5 ± 0.1	10.86	75–150	CF_3COCF_3	14
$C_6H_5CH_2Cl$		8.0 ± 0.3	12.46	67–151	CF_3COCF_3	14
$C_6H_5CCl_3$		8.8 ± 0.6	12.55	104–171	CF_3COCF_3	14
$C_6F_5CH_3$		6.38	10.75		CF_3COCF_3	15
Aldehydes						
CH_3CHO		4.2	10.84	170–250	CF_3CHO	5
CF_3CHO		8.4	11.73	150–400	CF_3CHO	5
Ketones						
CH_3COCH_3		8.0	11.51	250–320	$CF_3N_2CF_3$	2
		6.9 ± 0.1	10.77	29–169	CF_3COCF_3	16
		8.27 ± 0.17	11.52 ± 0.08	85–240	CF_3COCF_3	17, 16
CF_3COCH_3		6.6	11.3	25–350	CF_3COCH_3	18
$C_6H_5COCF_3$		7.2 ± 0.5	9.7	158–304	$C_6H_5COCF_3$	19
Halogenated Methanes						
CH_3Cl		10.6 ± 0.2	12.11 ± 0.08	144–400	CF_3COCF_3	8
CH_2Cl_2		7.6 ± 0.1	11.19 ± 0.08	85–204	CF_3COCF_3	20
$CHCl_3$		6.6 ± 0.1	11.04 ± 0.06	94–296	CF_3COCF_3	20
		5.3 ± 0.1	10.16 ± 0.07	35–338	$CF_3N_2CF_3$	21
		6.3 ± 0.6	11.98	118–251	CF_3COCF_3	7

Reactants	Notes	E	$\log_{10}A$	Temperature range	Radical source	Reference
		(*kcal mole*$^{-1}$)	(*mole*$^{-1}$ *cc. sec*$^{-1}$)	°C		
$CDCl_3$		9.0 ± 0.4	11.78	65–264	CF_3COCF_3	7
CH_3Br	(d)	10.9 ± 0.3	12.19 ± 0.14	150–260	CF_3COCF_3	8
	(e)	9.9 ± 0.1	11.63 ± 0.06	150–260	CF_3COCF_3	8
CH_3I		7.5 ± 0.3	10.63 ± 0.16	55–210	CF_3COCF_3	8
Hydrogen halides and hydrogen sulphide						
HCl		5.1 ± 0.5	11.05	20–205	CF_3COCF_3	26
HBr		2.9 ± 0.5	11.78		CF_3COCF_3	26
		$k = 3.0 \times 10^8$		26	CF_3COCF_3	22
H_2S		3.88 ± 0.26	11.65 ± 0.16	63–100	CF_3COCF_3	27

CHLORINE ATOM TRANSFER (i)

Reactants	Notes	E	$\log_{10}A$	Temperature range	Radical source	Reference
Cl_2		3.6 ± 0.5	12.89	126–235	CF_3COCF_3	26
CH_3Cl		$\geqslant 17$			CF_3COCF_3	20
CH_2Cl_2		11.8 ± 0.7	11.49 ± 0.1	306–449	CF_3COCF_3	20
$CHCl_3$	(f)	12.0 ± 0.2	12.08 ± 0.1	95–296	CF_3COCF_3	20
		11.0 ± 0.4	11.33 ± 0.2	35–338	$CF_3N_2CF_3$	21
CCl_4		9.3 ± 0.4	11.79 ± 0.2	122–288	$CF_3N_2CF_3$	21
		10.4 ± 0.1	12.57 ± 0.04	96–240	CF_3COCF_3	20
C_6H_5Cl		$\geqslant 13$		20–118	CF_3COCF_3	14
$C_6H_5CH_2Cl$		$\geqslant 13$		67–151	CF_3COCF_3	14
$C_6H_5CCl_3$		9.7 ± 0.5	12.49	104–171	CF_3COCF_3	14

BROMINE ATOM TRANSFER

Reactants	Notes	E	$\log_{10}A$	Temperature range	Radical source	Reference
Br_2		0.7 ± 0.5	12.36	178–327	CF_3COCF_3	26
CH_3Br	(d)	8.4 ± 0.1	10.83 ± 0.06	150–260	CF_3COCF_3	8
	(e)	8.1 ± 0.2	10.41 ± 0.10	150–260	CF_3COCF_3	8
C_6H_5Br	(g)	1.7 ± 1.1	7.91	23–95	CF_3COCF_3	14
C_6F_5Br	(g)	0.3 ± 0.6	7.38	39–107	CF_3COCF_3	14
HBr	(a)	84.2	10.71	832–1011		23

247-168 O-67—5

Trifluoromethyl Radicals—Continued

Reactants	Notes	E	$\log_{10}A$	Tempera-ture range	Radical source	Reference
		(*kcal mole*$^{-1}$)	(*mole*$^{-1}$ *cc. sec*$^{-1}$)	°C		
			IODINE ATOM TRANSFER			
I_2		0.0 ± 0.5	12.42		CF_3COCF_3	26
CH_3I		3.3 ± 0.15	9.59 ± 0.08	55–210	CF_3COCF_3	8
C_6H_5I		3.1 ± 0.6	10.33	75–150	CF_3COCF_3	14
			OXYGEN ATOM TRANSFER			
N_2O	(h)	24.0	13.15	316–375	CF_3COCF_3	24

Ratios of Rate Constants (Trifluoromethyl Radicals)

Reaction	Notes	E_1-E_2	$\log_{10}A_1/A_2$	Tempera-ture range	Radical source	Reference
		(*kcal mole*$^{-1}$)		°C		
(1) $CF_3+Br_2 = CF_3Br+Br$ (2) $CF_3+HBr = CF_3H+Br$		−0.52 ± 1.88 −2.17 ± 0.16	0.93 ± 0.60 0.58 ± 0.08	361–431 55–334	CF_3H thermal bromination CF_3COCF_3	22 25
(1) $CF_3+I_2=CF_3I+I$ (2) $CF_3+HBr = CF_3H+Br$		−2.98 ± 0.12	0.64 ± 0.06	85–230	CF_3COCF_3	25
(1) $CF_3+CHD_3 = CF_3H+CD_3$ (2) $CF_3+CHD_3 = CF_3D+CHD_2$		−2.2	−0.29	55–354	CF_3COCF_3	9
(1) $CF_3+CH_2D_2 = CF_3H+CHD_2$ (2) $CF_3+CH_2D_2 = CF_3D+CH_2D$		$\ln k_1/k_2 = \ln 1.400 + 0.42\times10^6/T^2$		727–1067	$CF_3N_2CF_3$	28

Notes

(a) CF_3Br inhibition of H_2/O_2 shock tube ignition.
(b) Values less reliable than others quoted by the same authors.
(c) Results combined with data from reference 16.
(d) At low (25mm Hg) CH_3Br pressures.
(e) At high (180mm Hg) CH_3Br pressures.
(f) This result is preferred to that obtained with $CF_3N_2CF_3$.
(g) "A" factor unreasonable.
(h) Result described as "semi-quantitative."
(i) For data involving fluorine atom transfer, see reference 29.

References

1. Ayscough and Polanyi, Trans. Faraday Soc. **52,** 960 (1956).
2. Pritchard, Pritchard, Schiff, and Trotman-Dickenson, Trans. Faraday Soc. **52,** 849 (1956).
3. Skinner and Ringrose, J. Chem. Phys. **43,** 4129 (1965).
4. Ayscough, Polanyi, and Steacie, Can. J. Chem. **33,** 743 (1955).
5. Dodd and Smith, J. Chem. Soc. 1465 (1957).
6. Pritchard, Pritchard, and Trotman-Dickenson, Chem. and Ind. 564 (1955).
7. Carmichael and Johnston, J. Chem. Phys. **41,** 1975 (1964).

8. Alcock and Whittle, Trans. Faraday Soc. **61,** 244 (1965).
9. Sharp and Johnston, J. Chem. Phys. **37,** 1541 (1962).
10. Ayscough and Steacie, Can. J. Chem. **34,** 103 (1956).
11. Charles and Whittle, Trans. Faraday Soc. **52,** 849 (1956).
12. Holmes and Kutschke, Trans. Faraday Soc. **58,** 333 (1962).
13. Charles, Pearson, and Whittle, Trans. Faraday Soc. **57,** 1356 (1961).
14. Giles and Whittle, Trans. Faraday Soc. **62,** 128 (1966).
15. Charles, Pearson, and Whittle, Trans. Faraday Soc. **59,** 1156 (1963).
16. Pritchard and Dacey, Can. J. Chem. **38,** 182 (1960).
17. Giles and Whittle, Trans. Faraday Soc. **61,** 1425 (1965).
18. Sieger and Calvert, J. Am. Chem. Soc. **76,** 5197 (1954).
19. Smith and Calvert, J. Am. Chem. Soc. **78,** 2345 (1956).
20. Alcock and Whittle, Trans. Faraday Soc. **62,** 134 (1966).
21. Alcock and Whittle, Trans. Faraday Soc. **62,** 664 (1966).
22. Corbett, Tarr and Whittle, Trans. Faraday Soc. **59,** 1609 (1963).
23. Skinner and Ringrose, J. Chem. Phys. **43,** 4129 (1965).
24. Bell and Kutschke, Can. J. Chem. **42,** 2713 (1964).
25. Tucker and Whittle, Trans. Faraday Soc. **61,** 866 (1965).
26. Amphlett and Whittle, Trans. Faraday Soc. **62,** 1662 (1966).
27. Arthur and Bell, Can. J. Chem. **44,** 1445 (1966).
28. Johnston and Tschuikow-Roux, J. Chem. Phys. **36,** 463 (1962).
29. Stewart and Cady, J. Am. Chem. Soc. **77,** 6110 (1955).

Metathetical Reactions of Halogenated Methyl Radicals

Reactants	Notes	E	$\log_{10}A$	Temperature range	Radical source		Reference
			(i) Reactions of CFH_2 Radicals				
Hydrogen atom transfer		*(kcal mole^{-1})*	*(cm^3 mole^{-1} sec^{-1})*	*°C*			
CFH_2COCFH_2	(a)	8.0 ± 0.1	10.71	100–300	CFH_2COCFH_2	P	1
			(ii) Reactions of CF_2Cl Radicals				
Hydrogen atom transfer							
cyclo-C_5H_{10}	(b)	5.3 ± 0.4		50–227	$CF_2ClCOCF_2Cl$	P	2
Chlorine atom transfer							
$CF_2ClCOCF_2Cl$	(b)	4 ± 1		20–180	$CF_2ClCOCF_2Cl$	P	3
	(b)	~ 3		20–184	$CF_2ClCOCF_2Cl$	P	4
			(iii) Reactions of CCl_3 Radicals				
Hydrogen atom transfer							
H_2	(c)	11.3 ± 0.5	14.86	248–302	CCl_3Br	P	5
$\mathbf{CH_3}CH_2CH_2\mathbf{CH_3}$	(d)	11.2	10.1	146–257	CCl_3Br	P	6, 7
$CH_3\mathbf{CH_2CH_2}CH_3$	(d)	7 5	9.9	146–257	CCl_3Br	P	6, 7
HBr	(d)	$k = 2.76 \times 10^{11}$		190	CCl_3Br	P	6
Chlorine atom transfer							
Cl_2	(d)	5.3	12.86	70–155	$CHCl_3/Cl_2$	P	8, 9
CCl_3Br		18.6 ± 1		225–294	CCl_3Br	P	10
		17.4 ± 1		248–302	CCl_3Br	P	5
CCl_3COCCl_3		7 ± 1		107–252	CCl_3COCCl_3	P	11

Ratios of Rate Constants (Trichloromethyl Radicals)

Reactants	Notes	$E_1 - E_2$	$\log_{10} A_1/A_2$	Temperature range	Radical source		Reference
		(kcal mole^{-1})		°C			
(1) $CCl_3 + n\text{-}C_4H_{10} = sec\text{-}C_4H_9 + CCl_3H$ (2) $CCl_3 + n\text{-}C_4H_{10} = p\text{-}C_4H_9 + CCl_3H$		-3.08 ± 0.46	0.43 ± 0.25	197–294	CCl_3Br	P	7
(1) $CCl_3 + i\text{-}C_4H_{10} = (CH_3)_3C + CCl_3H$ (2) $CCl_3 + n\text{-}C_4H_{10} = sec\text{-}C_4H_9 + CCl_3H$		-2.40	0.30	132–189	CCl_3Br	P	7

Notes

(a) Calculated assuming $k = 10^{14}$ cm^3 mole^{-1} sec^{-1} for the combination of CFH_2 radicals.

(b) Calculated assuming $k = 10^{14}$ cm^3 mole^{-1} sec^{-1} for the combination of CF_2Cl radicals.

(c) Calculated assuming $k = 10^{10.7}$ cm^3 mole^{-1} sec^{-1} for the combination of CCl_3 radicals.

(d) Calculated assuming $k = 10^{11.80}$ cm^3 mole^{-1} sec^{-1} for the combination of CCl_3 radicals.

References

1. Pritchard, Venugopalan, and Graham, J. Phys. Chem. **68,** 1786 (1964).
2. Majer, Phillips, and Robb, Trans. Faraday Soc. **61,** 122 (1965).
3. Bowles, Majer, and Robb, Trans. Faraday Soc. **58,** 1541 (1962).
4. Bowles, Majer, and Robb, Trans. Faraday Soc. **58,** 2394 (1962).
5. Hautecloque, Compt. Rend. **257,** 131 (1963).
6. Tedder and Watson, Trans. Faraday Soc. **62,** 1215 (1966).
7. McGrath and Tedder, Bull. Soc. Chim. Belges **71,** 772 (1962).
8. Chiltz, Martens, and Mahieu, Nature **180,** 1068 (1957).
9. Chiltz, Mahieu, and Martens, Bull. Soc. Chim. Belges **67,** 33 (1958).
10. Hautecloque, Compt. Rend. **256,** 2601 (1963).
11. Hautecloque, Compt. Rend. **254,** 3671 (1960).

Review

1. Chiltz, Goldfinger, Huybrechts, Martens, and Verbecke, Chem. Rev. **63,** 355 (1963).

Relative Rate Constants (Formyl Radicals)

Reactants	Notes	$E_1 - E_2$	$\log_{10} A_1/A_2$	k_1/k_2	Temperature range	Radical source		References
		(kcal mole^{-1})			°C			
(1) $HCO + NO_2 = HNO_2 + CO$ (2) $HCO + NO_2 = HCO_2 + NO$		0.65	0.5		100–220	CH_2O/NO_2	T	1, 2
(1) $HCO(+M) = CO + H(+M)$ (2) $HCO + O_2 = CO + HO_2$				2.7×10^{-9} cm^{-3} mole	36	CH_3COCH_3/O_2	P	3

References

1. Shaw, J. Chem. Soc. 1517 (1964).
2. Pollard and Wyatt, Trans. Faraday Soc. **45**, 760 (1949).
3. Pearson, J. Phys. Chem. **67**, 1686 (1963).

Metathetical Reactions of Methoxy Radicals

Reactants	Notes	E	$\log_{10} A$	Temperature range	Radical source	References
HYDROGEN ATOM TRANSFER						
Alkanes		(*kcal mole*$^{-1}$)	(*cm*^{3} *mole*$^{-1}$ *sec*$^{-1}$)	°*C*		
CH_4	(a)	11.0	11.8	125–250		15
C_2H_6	(b)	7.1	11.5	200–400	CH_3OOCH_3 T	1, 2, 3
C_3H_8	(b)	5.2	11.3	200–400	CH_3OOCH_3 T	1, 2, 3
n-C_4H_{10}	(c) (b)	2.9	10.5	200–400	CH_3OOCH_3 T	1, 2, 3
iso-C_4H_{10}	(b)	4.1	11.0	190–260	CH_3OOCH_3 T	1, 2, 3
$(CH_3)_4C$	(b)	7.3	11.8	200–300	CH_3OOCH_3 T	1, 2
Cyclo-Alkanes						
cyclo-C_3H_6	(b)	9.7	12.2	200–400	CH_3OOCH_3 T	1, 2
Esters						
$HCOOCH_3$		8.2	12.2	124–185	CH_3OOCH_3 T	4, 5
CH_3COOCH_3		~4.5		63–216	CH_3COOCH_3 P	6, 14
CH_3COOCD_3	(d)	~5		30–201	CH_3COOCD_3 P	7, 14

Ratios of Rate Constants (Methoxy Radicals)

Reactants	Notes	E_1-E_2	$\log_{10} A_1/A_2$	Temperature range	Radical source	References
		(*kcal mole*$^{-1}$)		°*C*		
(1) CH_3O+CH_3OH $=CH_3OH+CH_2OH$ (2) $CH_3O+HCHO$ $=CH_3OH+HCO$		$3.0-4.3$		155–180	CH_3OOCH_3 P	8, 12
(1) $CH_3O+HCHO$ $=CH_3OH+HCO$ (2) $2CH_3O=CH_3OH$ $+HCHO$	(f)	$k_1/k_2^{1/2}=10^{3.68}\exp(-3000/RT)$		50–135	D.T.B.P. T, P	9
(1) $CH_3O+O_2=CH_2O$ $+HO_2$ (2) $2CH_3O=CH_3OH$ $+CH_2O$	(f)	$k_1/k_2^{1/2}=0.59$		room temp.	CH_3I/O_2 P	10
(1) $CH_3+CH_2(OCH_3)_2$ $=CH_3OH+[C_3H_7O_2]$ (2) $CH_3O=H+CO+H_2$		$k_1/k_2=1.14\times10^5$ cm^3 mole^{-1}		459	$CH_2(OCH_3)_2$ T	11

Notes

(a) Calculated from the back reaction.

(b) The A factors were deduced by a semi-empirical method by Berces and Trotman-Dickenson (ref. 1). The original work contained an arithmetical mistake that resulted in an overestimate of log A of 0.3 units.

(c) This value seems likely to be incorrect.

(d) The reactant radical in this case is CD_3O.

(e) For further data on methoxy radicals see reference 13.

(f) Units are $cm^{3/2}$ $mole^{-1/2}$ $sec^{-1/2}$.

References

1. Berces and Trotman-Dickenson, J. Chem. Soc. 348 (1961).
2. Shaw and Trotman-Dickenson, J. Chem. Soc. 3210 (1960).
3. Shaw and Trotman-Dickenson, Proc. Chem. Soc. 61 (1959).
4. Thynne and Gray, Trans. Faraday Soc. **59,** 1149 (1963).
5. Thynne and Gray, Proc. Chem. Soc. 295 (1962).
6. Wijnen, J. Chem. Phys. **27,** 710 (1957).
7. Wijnen, J. Chem. Phys. **28,** 939 (1958).
8. Takezaki and Takeuchi, J. Chem. Phys. **22,** 1527 (1954).
9. Hoare and Wellington, 8th. Int. Comb. Symp., p. 472 (Williams and Wilkins, 1962).
10. Heicklen and Johnston, J. Am. Chem. Soc. **84,** 4030 (1962).
11. Molera, Fernandez-Biarge, Centeno, and Arevalo, J. Chem. Soc. 2311 (1963).
12. Takezaki, Miyazaki, and Nakahara, J. Chem. Phys. **25,** 536 (1956).
13. Dever and Calvert, J. Am. Chem. Soc. **84,** 1362 (1962).
14. Wijnen, J. Chem. Phys. **28,** 271 (1958).
15. Shaw and Thynne, Trans. Faraday Soc. **62,** 104 (1966).

Reviews

1. Gray and Williams, Chem. Rev. **59,** 239 (1959).

Metathetical Reactions of Methylthio Radicals

Reactants	Note	E	$\log_{10} A$	Temperature range	Radical source		References
HYDROGEN ATOM TRANSFER							
		(*kcal mole*$^{-1}$)	(*cm*^{3} *mole*$^{-1}$ *sec*$^{-1}$)	°C			
CH_4	(a)	18.2	12.1	130–200			1
CH_3CHO		6.8	11.9	189–396	CH_3CHO/CH_3SH	P	2
		4.8	12.0	400–440	CH_3CHO/CH_3SH	T	3

Notes

(a) Calculated from the reverse reactions.

References

1. Greig and Thynne, Trans. Faraday Soc. **62,** 379 (1966).
2. Birrell, Smith, Trotman-Dickenson, and Wilkie, J. Chem. Soc. 2807 (1957).
3. Imai and Toyama, Bull. Chem. Soc. Japan **33,** 1408 (1960).

Reactions of Chloroformyl Radicals

Reactions	Notes	E	$\log_{10} A$	Temperature range	Radical source	References
		(kcal mole^{-1})	*(cm^3 mole^{-1} sec^{-1})*	°C		
$COCl + Cl_2 = COCl_2$ $+ Cl$		2.96	12.4	25–55	CO/Cl_2 P	1
	(a)	3.1	10.8	15–450		5
$COCl + NOCl = Cl_2$ $+ CO + NO$ (or $COCl_2 + NO$)		1.14	13.68	25–55	$CO/Cl_2/NOCl$ P	2
$COCl + O_2 = CO_2$ $+ ClO$		3.3	10.9	20–200	$Cl_2/O_2/CO$ P	3, 4

Notes

(a) Review of literature data.

References

1. Burns and Dainton, Trans. Faraday Soc. **48,** 39 (1952).
2. Burns and Dainton, Trans. Faraday Soc. **48,** 52 (1952).
3. Rollefson, J. Am. Chem. Soc. **55,** 148 (1933).
4. Trotman-Dickenson, "Gas Kinetics," p. 259 et seq. (Butterworths, 1955).
5. Bodenstein, Brenschede, and Schumacher, Z. Phys. Chem. **40B,** 121 (1938).

Metathetical Reactions of Cyano Radicals

Reactions	Notes	E	$\log_{10} A$	Temperature range	Radical source	References
		(*kcal mole*$^{-1}$)	(*cm*^{3} *mole*$^{-1}$ *sec*$^{-1}$)	°C		
$H_2 + CN = HCN + H$		~7			D.F.	1
$ClCN + CN = C_2N_2 + Cl$		6.0	13.05	1727–2527	ClCN S.T.	2
$C_2N_2 + CN =$ products		2.1	10.86	28–174	C_2N_2 F.P.	3
$O_2 + CN = NCO + O$		$k = 4.6 \times 10^{12}$		room temp.	C_2N_2/O_2 F.P.	5
		$k = 5.5 \times 10^{12}$		room temp.	C_2N_2/O_2 F.P.	3

Ratios of Rate Constants

Reactions	Notes	$E_1 - E_2$	$\log_{10} A_1/A_2$	k_1/k_2	Temperature range	Radical source	References
		(*kcal mole*$^{-1}$)			°C		
(1) $CH_4 + CN = CH_3 + HCN$ (2) $C_2H_6 + CN = C_2H_5 + HCN$		3.7 ± 0.2	1.31		30–150	ICN P	4
(1) $C_2H_6 + CN = C_2H_5 + HCN$ (2) $C_3H_8 + CN = n\text{-}C_3H_7 + HCN$		-0.1 ± 0.2	0.00		30–150	ICN P	4
(1) $C_2H_6 + CN = C_2H_5 + HCN$ (2) $C_3H_8 + CN = i\text{-}C_3H_7 + HCN$		-0.1 ± 0.3	0.04		30–150	ICN P	4
(1) $C_3H_8 + CN = n\text{-}C_3H_7 + HCN$ (2) $C_3H_8 + CN = i\text{-}C_3H_7 + HCN$		-0.1 ± 0.3	0.08		30–150	ICN P	4

References

1. Hartel and Polanyi, Z. Phys. Chem. **B11**, 97 (1930).
2. Schofield, Tsang, and Bauer, J. Chem. Phys. **42**, 2132 (1965).
3. Paul and Dalby, J. Chem. Phys. **37**, 592 (1962).
4. Goy, Shaw, and Pritchard, J. Phys. Chem. **69**, 1504 (1965).
5. Basco, Proc. Roy. Soc. **283A**, 302 (1965).

Ratios of Rate Constants (Ethynyl Radicals)

(i) Reactions of the type (1) $C_2H + RH = C_2H_2 + R$
(2) $C_2H + BrC_2H = C_4H_2 + Br$.

RH	Notes	k_1/k_2	Temperature	Radical source	References
Alkanes			°C		
CH_4		0.020	27	BrC_2H P	1
C_2H_6		0.40	27	BrC_2H P	1
n-C_4H_{10}		1.05	27	BrC_2H P	1
iso-C_4H_{10}		1.25	27	BrC_2H P	1
$(CH_3)_4C$		1.1	27	BrC_2H P	1
$(CH_3)_3C.C(CH_3)_3$		1.2	27	BrC_2H P	1
Cyclo-alkanes					
cyclo-C_3H_6		0.21	27	BrC_2H P	1
cyclo-C_4H_8		1.35	27	BrC_2H P	1
spiro-C_5H_8		0.64	27	BrC_2H P	1
cyclo-C_5H_{10}		2.1	27	BrC_2H P	1
cyclo-C_6H_{12}		3.2	27	BrC_2H P	1
cyclo-C_6D_{12}		2.3	27	BrC_2H P	1
Halogenated alkanes					
C_2H_5Cl		0.14	27	BrC_2H P	1

(ii) Reactions of the type (1) $C_2H + RH = C_2H_2 + R$
(2) $C_2H + CH_2{:}CHCH_2CH_3 = C_2H_2 + C_4H_7$

RH	Notes	k_1/k_2	Temperature	Radical source	Reference
Alkenes			°C		
$CH_2{:}CHCH_3$		0.63	27	BrC_2H P	2
cis-$CH_3CH{:}CHCH_3$		1.04	27	BrC_2H P	2
trans-$CH_3CH{:}CHCH_3$		1.06	27	BrC_2H P	2
$CH_2{:}C(CH_3)_2$		0.90	27	BrC_2H P	2
$CH_2{:}CHCH_2CH_2CH_3$		1.7	27	BrC_2H P	2
$CH_2{:}CHCH(CH_3)_2$		1.22	27	BrC_2H P	2

References

1. Tarr, Strausz, and Gunning, Trans. Faraday Soc. **61,** 1946 (1965).

2. Tarr, Strausz, and Gunning, Trans. Faraday Soc. **62,** 1221 (1966).

Metathetical Reactions of Ethyl Radicals

Reactants	Notes	E	$\log_{10} A$	Temperature range	Radical source		Reference
			HYDROGEN ATOM TRANSFER				
Hydrogen		*(kcal mole^{-1})*	*(cm^3 mole^{-1} sec^{-1})*	°C			
H_2	(a)	11.5 ± 1					1
		4.05	12.19	752–917	H_2/O_2 ignition	S.T.	2
	(b)	11.3 ± 0.5	11.51	83–322	$(C_2D_5)_2CO$	P	3
		15.9	12.8				
D_2		13.3 ± 0.5	12.0	54–287	$(C_2H_5)_2CO$	P	1
Alkanes							
n-C_4H_{10}		15.2	11.77	420–530	n-C_4H_{10}	T	4
	(b)	10.4	11.03	106–325	$(C_2D_5)_2CO$	P	5
i-C_4H_{10}	(b)	8.9	10.62	87–319	$(C_2D_5)_2CO$	P	5
neo-C_5H_{12}	(b)	12.6	11.25	86–324	$(C_2D_5)_2CO$	P	5
cyclo-C_6H_{12}	(b)	10.4 ± 0.5	11.42 ± 0.2	99–293	$(C_2D_5)_2CO$	P	3
n-C_6H_{14}	(b)	10.1 ± 0.5	11.14 ± 0.2	87–252	$(C_2D_5)_2CO$	P	3
n-C_7H_{16}		10.6 ± 0.4	11.69 ± 0.2	124–200	$(C_2H_5)_2CO$	P	6
Alkenes							
1,5-C_6H_{10}		6.3 ± 0.4	10.1 ± 0.2	71–175	$(C_2H_5)_2CO$	P	7
1-C_7H_{14}		8.3 ± 0.5	11.19 ± 0.3	85–200	$(C_2H_5)_2CO$	P	6
1-C_8H_{16}		8.3 ± 0.2	11.19 ± 0.3	85–180	$(C_2H_5)_2CO$	P	6
		7.5 ± 0.5	10.6 ± 0.3	66–152	$(C_2H_5)_2CO$	P	9
trans 4-C_8H_{16}		8.7 ± 1.0	11.5 ± 0.6	85–165	$(C_2H_5)_2CO$	P	6
$(CH_3)_2C$:CHCH: $C(CH_3)_2$		7.6 ± 0.4	11.1 ± 0.2	53–147	$(C_2H_5)_2CO$	P	9
Cyclo alkenes							
cyclohexadiene,-1,3.		5.4 ± 0.5	10.6 ± 0.3	25–160	$(C_2H_5)_2CO$	P	9, 8
cyclohexadiene,-1,4.		5.8 ± 0.1	11.3 ± 0.1	50–140	$(C_2H_5)_2CO$	P	10
cyclohexene		8.2 ± 0.5	11.5 ± 0.3	23–250	$(C_2H_5)_2CO$	P	6
		7.5 ± 0.4	10.2 ± 0.2	40–210	$(C_2H_5)_2CO$	P	10
cycloheptatriene		6.5 ± 0.5	10.9 ± 0.3	50–130	$(C_2H_5)_2CO$	P	10
cyclooctatetraene		8.6 ± 1.2	11.6 ± 0.7	50–130	$(C_2H_5)_2CO$	P	10
cyclooctadiene,-1,5.		6.8 ± 0.7	10.9 ± 0.4	60–130	$(C_2H_5)_2CO$	P	10

Metathetical Reactions of Ethyl Radicals – Continued

Reactants	Notes	E	$\log_{10} A$	Temperature range	Radical source	Reference
		(*kcal mole*$^{-1}$)	(*cm*^{3} *mole*$^{-1}$ *sec*$^{-1}$)	°C		
Alkynes						
i-C_7H_{12}		7.6 ± 0.2	10.9 ± 0.1	23–180	$(C_2H_5)_2CO$ P	6
Aldehydes						
C_2H_5CHO		7.6 ± 1.0	11.5	134–156	D.T.B.P. T	11
		5.9	10.8	91–315	C_2H_5CHO P	12
		6.3		100–175	C_2H_5CHO P	12, 13
Ketones						
$CH_3COC_2H_5$		8.0 ± 0.1	11.0	79–234	$CH_3COC_2H_5$ P	16
$(C_2H_5)_2CO$		7.4	10.9	25–225	$(C_2H_5)_2CO$ P	14, 21
		7.6	11.0	41–158	$(C_2H_5)_2N_2$ P	15
		7.8 ± 0.2	11.1 ± 0.1	50–215	$(C_2H_5)_2CO$ P	6
		8.9	11.7	75–170	$(C_2H_5)_2CO$ P	17
$(C\mathbf{H}_3CD_2)_2CO$	(c)	11.7	11.4	24–365	$(CH_3CD_2)_2CO$ P	18
$(CH_3C\mathbf{D}_2)_2CO$	(c)	8.7	11.6	24–365	$(CH_3CD_2)_2CO$ P	18, 19
		9.2 ± 0.4	11.1 ± 0.1	24–365	$(CH_3CD_2)_2CO$ P	19
$(C_2D_5)_2CO$	(b)	9.6 ± 0.4	11.3	160–314	$(C_2D_5)_2CO$ P	19
		9.0 ± 0.5	10.95	50–324	$(C_2D_5)_2CO$ P	5
$C_2F_5COC_2H_5$		6.8	10.85	100–250	$C_2F_5COC_2H_5$ P	37
$C_3F_7COC_2H_5$		7.2	10.9	80–362	$C_3F_7COC_2H_5$ P	20
Esters						
$HCOOC_2H_5$		7.8	10.6	77–230	CH_3COCH_3 P	17
$C_2H_5COOC_2H_5$		9.8	11.5	108–344	$C_2H_5COOC_2H_5$ P	22
$C_2H_5COOCH_2CH{:}CH_2$		5.8 ± 1.4	9.7 ± 0.8	79–160	$(C_2H_5)_2CO$ P	23
Azo-compounds						
$(C_2H_5)_2N_2$		7.5	10.9	74–178	$(C_2H_5)_2N_2$ P	24
		8.0 ± 0.2	11.4	27–175	$(C_2H_5)_2N_2$ P	25
Metal alkyl						
$(C_2H_5)_2Hg$		6.2	10.3	75–200	$(C_2H_5)_2Hg$ P	26
Hydrogen halide						
HI		1.1	11.92	263–303	HI/C_2H_5I T	27

Metathetical Reactions of Ethyl Radicals—Continued

Reactants	Notes	E	$\log_{10} A$	Temperature range	Radical source		Reference
		(*kcal mole*$^{-1}$)	(*cm*^{3} *mole*$^{-1}$ *sec*$^{-1}$)	°C			
CHLORINE ATOM TRANSFER							
Cl_2		1.0	13.1				28
IODINE ATOM TRANSFER							
I_2	(d)	0.2	12.50	263–303	HI/C_2H_5I	T	27
OXYGEN ATOM TRANSFER							
N_2O	(e)	31.0	17.8	553–588	C_2H_6/N_2O	T	29

Ratios of Rate Constants (Ethyl Radicals)

Reaction	Notes	$E_1 - E_2$	$\log_{10} A_1/A_2$	k_1/k_2	Temperature range	Radical source		Reference
		(*kcal mole*$^{-1}$)			°C			
(1) $C_2H_5 + HBr = C_2H_6 + Br$ (2) $C_2H_5 + Br_2 = C_2H_5Br + Br$		0	−0.22		30–90	$C_2H_6/Br_2/HBr$	P	30, 36
(1) $C_2H_5 + HI = C_2H_6 + I$ (2) $C_2H_5 + I_2 = C_2H_5I + I$				0.15	260	C_2H_5I/HI	T	33, 32
				0.13 ± 0.03	250–280	C_2H_5I/HI	T	31, 32
		0.90	−0.58		263–303	C_2H_5I/HI	T	27
(1) $C_2H_5 + HBr = C_2H_6 + Br$ (2) $C_2H_5 + I_2 = C_2H_5I + I$		2.29 ± 0.08	0.23 ± 0.04		55–115	$CH_3COC_2H_5$	P	34
(1) $C_2H_5 + I_2 = C_2H_5I + I$ (2) $C_2H_5 + O_2 = C_2H_5O_2$				13	25	C_2H_5I/O_2	P	35
(1) $C_2H_5 + I_2 = C_2H_5I + I$ (2) $C_2H_5 + NO = C_2H_5NO$				7	25	C_2H_5I/NO	P	35

Notes

(a) Estimated from the reaction $D_2 + C_2H_5$, assuming the difference in activation energies to be equal to the difference of the zero-point energies.
(b) The attacking radical is C_2D_5.
(c) The attacking radical is CH_3CD_2.
(d) Calculated, assuming the activation energy of 0.2 kcal/mole.
(e) This *A* factor seems improbably high.

References

1. Wijnen and Steacie, J. Chem. Phys. **20,** 205 (1952).
2. Skinner and Ringrose, J. Chem. Phys. **43,** 4129 (1965).
3. Boddy and Steacie, Can. J. Chem. **39,** 13 (1961).
4. Purnell and Quinn, Proc. Roy. Soc. **270A,** 267 (1962).
5. Boddy and Steacie, Can. J. Chem. **38,** 1576 (1960).
6. James and Steacie, Proc. Roy. Soc. **244A,** 289 (1958).
7. James and Troughton, Trans. Faraday Soc. **62,** 145 (1966).

8. Brown and James, Proc. Chem. Soc. 81 (1962).
9. Brown and James, Can. J. Chem. **43,** 1102 (1965).
10. Brown and James, Can. J. Chem. **43,** 660 (1965).
11. Volman and Brinton, J. Chem. Phys. **22,** 929 (1954).
12. Kerr and Trotman-Dickenson, J. Chem. Soc. 1611 (1960).
13. Blacet and Pitts, J. Am. Chem. Soc. **74,** 3382 (1952).
14. Kutschke, Wijnen, and Steacie, J. Am. Chem. Soc. **74,** 714 (1952).
15. Ausloos and Steacie, Can. J. Chem. **32,** 593 (1954).
16. Ausloos and Steacie, Can. J. Chem. **33,** 1062 (1955).
17. Thynne, Trans. Faraday Soc. **58,** 676 (1962).
18. Wijnen and Steacie, Can. J. Chem. **29,** 1092 (1951).
19. James and Steacie, Proc. Roy. Soc. **245A,** 470 (1958).
20. Pritchard and Thommarson, J. Phys. Chem. **69,** 1001 (1965).
21. Brinton and Steacie, Can. J. Chem. **33,** 1840 (1955).
22. Wijnen, J. Am. Chem. Soc. **80,** 2394 (1958).
23. James and Troughton, Trans. Faraday Soc. **62,** 120 (1966).
24. Ausloos and Steacie, Bull. Soc. Chim. Belges. **63,** 87 (1954).
25. Cerfontain and Kutschke, Can. J. Chem. **36,** 344 (1958).
26. Ivin and Steacie, Proc. Roy. Soc. **208A,** 25 (1951).
27. Hartley and Benson, J. Chem. Phys. **39,** 132 (1963).
28. Goldfinger, Huybrechts, Martens, Meyers, and Olbrechts, Trans. Faraday Soc. **61,** 1933 (1965).
29. Kenright and Trenwith, J. Chem. Soc. 2079 (1959).
30. Anderson and Van Artsdalen, J. Chem. Phys. **12,** 479 (1944).
31. Sullivan, J. Phys. Chem. **65,** 722 (1961).
32. Ogg, J. Am. Chem. Soc. **56,** 526 (1934).
33. Benson and O'Neal, J. Chem. Phys. **34,** 514 (1961).
34. Fettis and Trotman-Dickenson, J. Chem. Soc. 3037 (1961).
35. Christie and Frost, Trans. Faraday Soc. **61,** 468 (1965).
36. Benson and Buss, J. Chem. Phys. **28,** 301 (1958).
37. Thommarson and Pritchard, J. Phys. Chem. **70,** 2307 (1966).

Perfluoroethyl Radicals

Reactants	Notes	E	$\log_{10} A$	Temperature range	Radical source	Reference
HYDROGEN ATOM TRANSFER						
		(kcal mole⁻¹)	*(mole⁻¹ cc sec⁻¹)*	°C		
H_2		11.9	12.72	137–237	$(C_2F_5)_2CO$	1
	(a)	12.4 ± 0.2	13.20	146–313	C_2F_5CHO	2
D_2	(a)	12.6 ± 0.2	12.45	135–339	C_2F_5CHO	2
		14.1 ± 0.3	13.08	154–259	$(C_2F_5)_2N_2$	3
CH_4		10.6	11.62	150–272	$(C_2F_5)_2CO$	1
C_2H_6		8.7 ± 0.2	12.18	84–226	$(C_2F_5)_2N_2$	3
cyclo-C_6H_{12}		6.0 ± 0.2	12.18	28–132	$(C_2F_5)_2N_2$	3
CF_3CHO		9.7 ± 0.2	12.40	138–220	$(C_2F_5)_2N_2$	3
C_2F_5CHO		4.5 ± 0.2	10.49	27–307	C_2F_5CHO	4
		4.9 ± 0.2	10.74	135–339	C_2F_5CHO	2
CH_3COCH_3		8.4 ± 0.2	11.71	82–220	$(C_2F_5)_2N_2$	3
$C_2F_5COC_2H_5$		5.6 ± 0.2	11.34	50–250	$C_2F_5COC_2H_5$	5

Notes

(a) These results are less reliable than those obtained from perfluoro ketone systems.

References

1. Price and Kutschke, Can. J. Chem. **38,** 2128 (1960).
2. Pritchard and Foote, J. Phys. Chem. **68,** 1016 (1964).
3. Pritchard, Dacey, Kent, and Simonds, Can. J. Chem. **44,** 171 (1966).
4. Pritchard, Miller, and Foote, Can. J. Chem. **40,** 1830 (1962).
5. Thommarson and Pritchard, J. Phys. Chem. **70,** 2307 (1966).

247-168 O-67—6

Metathetical Reactions of Halogenated Ethyl Radicals

Reactions	Notes	E	$\log_{10} A$	Temperature range	Radical source	Reference
		(kcal mole⁻¹)	*(cm³ mole⁻¹ sec⁻¹)*	°C		
$CH_2CH_2Cl + Cl_2 = CH_2ClCH_2Cl + Cl$		0			$CH_2{:}CH_2/Cl_2$ P	1, 2
$C_2H_3Cl_2 + Cl_2 = CH_2ClCHCl_2 + Cl$	(c)	0.92 ± 0.05	11.75 ± 0.2	25–55	$CH_2{:}CHCl/Cl_2$ P	1, 2, 3
$CHCl_2CHCl + Cl_2 = CHCl_2CHCl_2 + Cl$		2.74 ± 0.6	11.7 ± 0.3	30–65	cis-$CHCl{:}CHCl/Cl_2$ P	4, 3
$C_2HCl_4 + Cl_2 = CHCl_2CCl_3 + Cl$	(b)	5.1 ± 0.2	11.5 ± 0.2	80–140	$CHCl{:}CCl_2/Cl_2$ P	5, 3, 12
$C_2Cl_5 + Cl_2 = C_2Cl_6 + Cl$	(a)	5.5	11.3	87–247	$CCl_2{:}CCl_2/Cl_2$ P	6, 7
$CF_2CF_2Cl + Cl_2 = CF_2ClCF_2Cl + Cl$	(d)	0.8		30–60	$CF_2{:}CF_2/Cl_2$ P	13
$C_2F_3Cl_2 + Cl_2 = C_2F_3Cl_3 + Cl$	(e)	2.3		30–60	$CF_2{:}CFCl/Cl_2$ P	13
$CFCl_2CFCl + Cl_2 = CFCl_2CFCl_2 + Cl$	(f)	5.35 ± 0.3		30–70	$CFCl{:}CFCl/Cl_2$ P	14
$C_2F_4Br + HBr = C_2F_4Br_2 + H$		51.2	13.07	855–1013	$H_2/O_2/C_2F_4Br_2$ S.T.	15

Ratios of Rate Constants (Halogenated Ethyl Radicals)

Reactions	Notes	$E_1 - E_2$	$\log_{10} A_1/A_2$	k_1/k_2	Temperature range	Radical source	References
		(kcal mole⁻¹)			°C		
(1) $C_2H_4Br = C_2H_4 + Br$ (2) $C_2H_4Br + HBr = C_2H_5Br + Br$		14 ± 2			25–54	C_2H_4/HBr γ radiation	16, 18
(1) $C_2H_4Br = C_2H_4 + Br$ (2) $C_2H_4Br + Br_2 = C_2H_4Br_2 + Br$		6.1			60–80	C_2H_4/Br_2 P	17

Notes

(a) Data on this reaction can also be found in references 8 to 11.

(b) The reactant radical is probably $CHCl_2CCl_2^2$.

(c) The reactant radical is probably $CH_2ClCHCl^2$.

(d) Calculated assuming zero activation energy for the combination of CF_2CF_2Cl radicals.

(e) Calculated assuming zero activation energy for the combination of $C_2F_3Cl_2$ radicals.

(f) Calculated assuming zero activation energy for the combination of $CFCl_2CFCl$ radicals.

References

1. Dainton, Lomax, and Weston, Trans. Faraday Soc. **58,** 308 (1962).
2. Ayscough, Cocker, Dainton, and Hirst, Trans. Faraday Soc. **58,** 318 (1962).
3. Ayscough, Cocker, Dainton, Hirst, Lomax, and Weston, Proc. Chem. Soc. 244 (1961).
4. Ayscough, Cocker, Dainton, and Hirst, Trans. Faraday Soc. **58,** 295 (1962).
5. Dainton, Lomax, and Weston, Trans. Faraday Soc. **53,** 460 (1957).
6. Dusoleil, Goldfinger, Maheiu-Van der Auwera, Martens, and Van der Auwera, Trans. Faraday Soc. **57,** 2197 (1961).
7. Adam, Goldfinger, and Gosselain, Bull. Soc. Chim. Belges **65,** 549 (1956).
8. Adam and Goldfinger, Bull. Soc. Chim. Belges **65,** 561 (1956).
9. Adam, Dusoleil, and Goldfinger, Bull. Soc. Chim. Belges **65,** 942 (1956).
10. Ackerman, Chiltz, Goldfinger, and Martens, Bull. Soc. Chim. Belges **66,** 325 (1957).
11. Chiltz, Maheiu, and Martens, Bull. Soc. Chim. Belges **67,** 33 (1958).
12. Chiltz, Dusoleil, Goldfinger, Huybrechts, Mahieu, Martens, and Van der Auwera, Bull. Soc. Chim. Belges **68,** 5 (1959).
13. Castellano, Bergamin, and Schumacher, Z. Phys. Chem. **27,** 112 (1961).
14. Vallana, Castellano, and Schumacher, Z. Phys. Chem. **46,** 294 (1965).
15. Skinner and Ringrose, J. Chem. Phys. **43,** 4129 (1965).
16. Armstrong and Spinks, Can. J. Chem. **37,** 1210 (1959).
17. Schmitz, Schumacher, and Jager, Z. Phys. Chem. **51B,** 281 (1942).
18. Oldershaw and Cvetanovic, J. Chem. Phys. **41,** 3639 (1964).

Review

1. Chiltz, Goldfinger, Huybrechts, Martens, and Verbecke, Chem. Rev. **63,** 355 (1963).

Ratios of Rate Constants (Carbonylcarbene Radicals)

Ratios of the form (1) $CCO + C_3O_2 = \text{Polymer} + nCO$
(2) $CCO + C_nH_{2n} = C_{n+1}H_{2n} + CO$

Where C_nH_{2n} is an olefine, and $C_{n+1}H_{2n}$ is the diene and/or alkyne formed by addition of a carbon atom

Olefine	Notes	k_1/k_2	Temperature	Radical source		Reference
C_2H_4	(a)	1.4	0	C_3O_2	P	1
	(a)	1.26	0	C_3O_2	P	2
	(b)	2.79	0	C_3O_2	P	2
$CH_3CH{:}CH_2$	(a)	3.93	0	C_3O_2	P	2
	(b)	9.72	0	C_3O_2	P	2
$CH_2{:}CHCH_2CH_3$	(a)	13.14	0	C_3O_2	P	2
	(b)	38.91	0	C_3O_2	P	2
$CH_2{:}C(CH_3)_2$	(a)	14.04	0	C_3O_2	P	2
cis-$CH_3CH{:}CHCH_3$	(a)	8.03	0	C_3O_2	P	2
trans-$CH_3CH{:}CHCH_3$	(a)	14.33	0	C_3O_2	P	2
$(CH_3)_2C{:}CHCH_3$	(a)	34.38	0	C_3O_2	P	2
$(CH_3)_2C{:}C(CH_3)_2$	(a)	67.20	0	C_3O_2	P	2

Notes

(a) Photolysis at 2537 Å.
(b) Photolysis at >3100 Å.

References

1. Bayes, J. Am. Chem. Soc. **84**, 4077 (1962).
2. Baker, Kerr, and Trotman-Dickenson, J. Chem. Soc. 975A (1966).

Metathetical Reactions of Acetyl Radicals

Reactants	Notes	E	$\log_{10}A$	Temperature range	Radical source		Reference
		(kcal mole^{-1})	*(cm^3 mole^{-1} sec^{-1})*	°C			
$I_2 + CH_3CO$ $= CH_3COI + I$		0	12.6	222–268	CH_3COI/HI	T	1

Ratios of Rate Constants (Acetyl and Trifluoroacetyl Radicals)

Reaction	Notes	$E_1 - E_2$	$\log_{10}A_1/A_2$	k_1/k_2	Temperature range	Radical source		Reference
		(kcal mole^{-1})			°C			
(1) $CH_3CO = CH_3 + CO$ (2) $CH_3CO + HBr$ $= CH_3CHO + Br$		~13			100–300	CH_3COCH_3	P	2
(1) $CH_3CO = CH_3 + CO$ (2) $CH_3CO + O_2 = CH_3O + CO_2$		~9	−4.68 (mole cm^{-3})			CH_3COCH_3/O_2	P	3
(1) $CH_3CO + HI = CH_3CHO + I$ (2) $CH_3CO + I_2 = CH_3COI + I$		1.5	−0.47		222–268	CH_3COI/HI	T	1
(1) $CF_3CO = CF_3 + CO$ (2) $CF_3CO + Br_2$ $= CF_3COBr + Br$	(a)	6.0	−4.7		19–251	CF_3COCF_3/Br_2	P	4

Notes

(a) Values very doubtful.

References

1. O'Neal and Benson, J. Chem. Phys. **37**, 540 (1962).
2. Ridge and Steacie, Can. J. Chem. **33**, 383 (1955).
3. Cerfontain and Kutschke, J. Am. Chem. Soc. **84**, 4017 (1962).
4. Tucker and Whittle, Trans. Faraday Soc. **61**, 484 (1965).

Ratios of Rate Constants (Ethoxy Radicals)

Reactions	Notes	E_1-E_2	$\log_{10}A_1/A_2$	k_1/k_2	Temperature range	Radical source		Reference
		(*kcal mole*$^{-1}$)			°C			
(1) $C_2H_5O+(C_2H_5)_2CO = C_2H_5OH + C_2H_4COC_2H_5$ (2) $C_2H_5O+O_2 = CH_3CHO+HO_2$				0.1 ± 0.05	35	$(C_2H_5)_2CO/O_2$	P	1
(1) $C_2H_5O+(C_2H_5)_2N_2 = C_2H_5OH + C_2H_4N_2C_2H_5$ (2) $C_2H_5O+O_2 = CH_3CHO+HO_2$				0.6 ± 0.3	118	$(C_2H_5)_2N_2/O_2$	P	2
				1.1 ± 0.4	152	$(C_2H_5)_2N_2/O_2$	P	2
(1) $C_2H_5O=CH_3+CH_2O$ (2) $C_2H_5O+C_2H_5COOC_2H_5 = C_2H_5OH+C_5H_9O_2$		7.5 ± 1			29–195	$C_2H_5COOC_2H_5$	P	3

NOTE: For further data on ethoxy radicals see reference 4.

References

1. Jolley, J. Am. Chem. Soc. **79**, 1537 (1957).
2. Cerfontain and Kutschke, J. Am. Chem. Soc. **84**, 4017 (1962).
3. Wijnen, J. Am. Chem. Soc. **82**, 3034 (1960).
4. Heicklen and Johnston, J. Am. Chem. Soc. **84**, 4394 (1962).

Review

1. Gray and Williams, Chem. Rev. **59**, 239 (1959).

Metathetical Reactions of Allyl Radicals

Reactants	Notes	E	$\log_{10}A$	Temperature range	Radical source		Reference
HYDROGEN ATOM TRANSFER							
		(kcal mole^{-1})	*(cm^3 mole^{-1} sec^{-1})*	°C			
cyclo-C_5H_{10}		31.8 ± 3.6		450–514	CD_3COCD_3	P	1
$C_6H_5CH_3$	(a)	14 to 17		459–592	CH_2:$CHCH_2Br$	T	2
CH_2:$CHCH_2CH(CH_3)_2$		12		450–530	CH_2:$CHCH_2CH$ $(CH_3)_2$	T	3

Note

(a) Calculated assuming a steric factor in the range 10^{-1} to 10^{-2}.

References

1. Gordon, Smith, and McNesby, J. Am. Chem. Soc. **81,** 5059 (1959).
2. Szwarc, Ghosh, and Sehon, J. Chem. Phys. **18,** 1142 (1950).
3. Taniewski, J. Chem. Soc. 7436 (1965).

Metathetical Reactions of *n*-Propyl Radicals [(a)]

Reactants	Notes	E	$\log_{10}A$	Temperature range	Radical source		Reference
HYDROGEN ATOM TRANSFER							
		(*kcal mole*$^{-1}$)	(*cm*^{3} *mole*$^{-1}$ *sec*$^{-1}$)	°*C*			
$n\text{-}C_3H_7\mathbf{CHO}$		6.7	11.0	98–361	$n\text{-}C_3H_7CHO$	P	1
$n\text{-}C_3\mathbf{H}_7CHO$		10.8	11.0	191–300	$n\text{-}C_3H_7CHO$	P	1
$(n\text{-}C_3H_7)_2CO$		6.5	10.4	55–161	$(n\text{-}C_3H_7)_2CO$	P	2
$HCOOCH_2CH_2CH_3$		7.6	10.9	74–178	CH_3COCH_3	P	3
$(n\text{-}C_3H_7)_2N_2$		7.9	11.3	25–291	$(n\text{-}C_3H_7)_2N_2$	P	4

Ratios of Rate Constants (*n*-Propyl Radicals)

Reactions	Notes	k_1/k_2	Temperature range	Radical source		Reference
			°*C*			
(1) $n\text{-}C_3H_7 + HI = C_3H_8 + I$ (2) $n\text{-}C_3H_7 + I_2 = C_3H_7I + I$		0.11	290	$n\text{-}C_3H_7I/HI$	T	5, 6
(1) $n\text{-}C_3H_7 + I_2 = C_3H_7I + I$ (2) $n\text{-}C_3H_7 + NO = C_3H_7NO$		11	25	$n\text{-}C_3H_7I/NO$	P	7
(1) $n\text{-}C_3H_7 + I_2 = C_3H_7I + I$ (2) $n\text{-}C_3H_7 + O_2 = C_3H_7O_2$		22	25	$n\text{-}C_3H_7I/O_2$	P	7

Note

(a) The rate constants are based on log k (cm^3 mole^{-1} sec^{-1}) $= 10^{13.4}$ for the combination of *n*-propyl radicals.

References

1. Kerr and Trotman-Dickenson, Trans. Faraday Soc. **55,** 921 (1959).
2. Masson, J. Am. Chem. Soc. **74,** 4731 (1952).
3. Thynne, Trans. Faraday Soc. **58,** 1394 (1962).
4. Kerr and Calvert, J. Am. Chem. Soc. **83,** 3391 (1961).
5. Benson and O'Neal, J. Chem. Phys. **34,** 514 (1961).
6. Ogg, J. Am. Chem. Soc. **56,** 526 (1934).
7. Christie and Frost, Trans. Faraday Soc. **61,** 468 (1965).

Metathical Reactions of Isopropyl Radicals [a]

Reactants	Notes	E	$\log_{10}A$	Temperature range	Radical source		Reference
HYDROGEN ATOM TRANSFER							
Hydrogen		*(kcal mole⁻¹)*	*(cm³ mole⁻¹ sec⁻¹)*	°C			
H_2		12.5		260–320	$CH_3CH{:}CH_2$	+H	1
Alkenes							
cyclohexadiene-1,4		6.5	11.4	75–136	$(i\text{-}C_3H_7)_2CO$	P	2
cyclohexadiene-1,3		7.1 ± 0.7	11.5 ± 0.4	42–133	$(i\text{-}C_3H_7)_2CO$	P	3
Aldehydes and Ketones							
$i\text{-}C_3\mathbf{H}_7CHO$		9.5	10.7	283–377	$i\text{-}C_3H_7CHO$	P	4
$i\text{-}C_3H_7C\mathbf{H}O$		6.3	10.8	117–354	$i\text{-}C_3H_7CHO$	P	4
$(i\text{-}C_3H_7)_2CO$		8.5 ± 0.1	11.1	100–400	$(i\text{-}C_3H_7)_2CO$	P	5
$[(CH_3)_2C\mathbf{D}]_2CO$	(b)	9.3 ± 0.3	10.6	200–400	$[(CH_3)_2CD]_2CO$	P	6
$[(C\mathbf{H}_3)_2CD]_2CO$	(b)	11.7 ± 1.1	11.3	300–400	$[(CH_3)_2CD]_2CO$	P	6
Ester							
$HCOOCH(CH_3)_2$		6.6	9.9	94–181	CH_3COCH_3	P	7
Azo-compound							
$(i\text{-}C_3H_7)_2N_2$		6.5 ± 0.5	9.9	30–120	$(i\text{-}C_3H_7)_2N_2$	P	8
		6.7 ± 0.4	10.0	35–127	$(i\text{-}C_3H_7)_2N_2$	P	9

Ratios of Rate Constants (Isopropyl Radicals)

Reactions	Notes	$E_1 - E_2$	$\log_{10}A_1/A_2$	k_1/k_2	Temperature range	Radical source		Reference
		(kcal mole⁻¹)			°C			
(1) $i\text{-}C_3H_7 + I_2 = C_3H_7I + I$ (2) $i\text{-}C_3H_7 + NO = C_3H_7NO$				22	25	$i\text{-}C_3H_7I/NO$	P	10
(1) $i\text{-}C_3H_7 + I_2 = C_3H_7I + I$ (2) $i\text{-}C_3H_7 + O_2 = C_3H_7O_2$				~3	25	$i\text{-}C_3H_7I/O_2$	P	10
(1) $i\text{-}C_3H_7 + i\text{-}C_3H_7I = C_3H_6 + C_3H_8 + I$	(c)			520(3130Å)	35	$i\text{-}C_3H_7I$	P	11
(2) $i\text{-}C_3H_7 + I_2 = i\text{-}C_3H_7I + I$	(c)			170(2300Å)	35	$i\text{-}C_3H_7I$	P	11
(1) $C_3H_7 + O_2 = C_3H_6 + HO_2$ (2) $C_3H_7 + O_2 = C_3H_7O_2$	(d)	19.0	6.6		345–472	C_3H_8/O_2	T	12

Notes

(a) The rate constants are based on log k ($cm^3\ mole^{-1}\ sec^{-1}$) $=10^{12.9}$ for the combination of isopropyl radicals.
(b) The attacking radical is $(CH_3)_2CD$.
(c) The difference in values is due to a hot radical effect. The value at 3130 Å approximates to the correct value for thermally equilibrated isopropyl radicals.
(d) Summary of a large body of literature data. The propyl radical is probably a mixture of n and isopropyl.

References

1. Hoey and Le Roy, Can. J. Chem. **33,** 580 (1955).
2. James and Suart, J. Am. Chem. Soc. **86,** 5424 (1964).
3. James and Suart, J. Phys. Chem. **69,** 2362 (1965).
4. Kerr and Trotman-Dickenson, Trans. Faraday Soc. **55,** 921 (1959).
5. Heller and Gordon, J. Phys. Chem. **60,** 1315 (1956).
6. Heller and Gordon, J. Phys. Chem. **62,** 709 (1958).
7. Thynne, Trans. Faraday Soc. **58,** 1394 (1962).
8. Durham and Steacie, Can. J. Chem. **31,** 377 (1953).
9. Riem and Kutschke, Can. J. Chem. **38,** 2332 (1960).
10. Christie and Frost, Trans. Faraday Soc. **61,** 468 (1965).
11. McMillan and Noyes, J. Am. Chem. Soc. **80,** 2108 (1958).
12. Sattersfield and Reid, J. Phys. Chem. **59,** 283 (1955).

Perfluoropropyl Radicals

Reactants	Notes	E	$\log_{10}A$	Temperature range	Radical source	Reference
			HYDROGEN ATOM TRANSFER			
		(kcal mole⁻¹)	*(mole⁻¹ cm³ sec⁻¹)*	°C		
H_2		12.3 ± 0.4	12.64	125–243	$(n\text{-}C_3F_7)_2CO$	1
	(a)	12.1 ± 0.2	12.86	157–319	C_3F_7CHO	2
D_2		13.8 ± 0.5	12.78		$(n\text{-}C_3F_7)_2CO$	1
	(b)	12.9 ± 0.8	12.69	85–182	$(n\text{-}C_3F_7)_2CO$	3
	(a)	14.0 ± 0.1	12.98	165–297	C_3F_7CHO	2
CH_4		9.5 ± 0.5	10.99	70–166	$(n\text{-}C_3F_7)_2CO$	3
C_2H_6	(c)	9.2 ± 0.5	12.24	87–196	$(n\text{-}C_3F_7)_2CO$	3
cyclo-C_6H_{12}		5.2 ± 0.1	11.08	25–290	$(n\text{-}C_3F_7)_2CO$	4
C_3F_7CHO	(c)	4.0 ± 0.3	10.27	28–315	C_3F_7CHO	5
		5.5 ± 0.2	10.98	165–297	C_3F_7CHO	2
CH_3COCH_3		7.2 ± 0.4	11.83	27–306	C_3F_7CHO	6
$C_3F_7COC_2H_5$		8.4 ± 0.3	11.77	80–362	$C_3F_7COC_2H_5$	7

Notes

(a) These results are less reliable than those obtained from perfluoro ketone systems.
(b) Assuming $k=10^{10.99}\exp(-9500/RT)$ for the reaction $n-C_3F_7+CH_4=C_3F_7H+CH_3$.
(c) For both these compounds it seems likely that errors have been made in the determination of the activation energies, although the rate constants were probably of the correct magnitude.

References

1. Miller and Steacie, J. Am. Chem. Soc. **80,** 6486 (1958).
2. Pritchard and Foote, J. Phys. Chem. **68,** 1016 (1964).
3. Giacometti and Steacie, Can. J. Chem. **36,** 1493 (1958).
4. Pritchard and Miller, J. Phys. Chem. **63,** 2074 (1959).
5. Pritchard, Miller, and Foote, Can. J. Chem. **40,** 1830 (1962).
6. Pritchard, Hsia, and Miller, J. Am. Chem. Soc. **85,** 1568 (1963).
7. Pritchard and Thommarson, J. Phys. Chem. **69,** 1001 (1965).

Metathetical Reactions of Halogenated Propyl Radicals

Reactions	Notes	E	$\log_{10}A$	Temperature range	Radical source		Reference
		(*kcal mole*$^{-1}$)	(*cm*^{3} *mole*$^{-1}$ *sec*$^{-1}$)	°C			
$CCl_3CH_2CH_2 + CCl_3Br$ $= CCl_3CH_2CH_2Br$ $+ CCl_3$		3.4	8	103–193	C_2H_4/CCl_3Br	P	1
$ICH_2CH_2CH_2 + I_2$ $= ICH_2CH_2CH_2I + I$	(a)	0.5	12.5		cyclo-C_3H_6/I_2	T	2

Note

(a) Estimated from the equilibrium constant and collision theory.

References

1. Tedder and Walton, Trans. Faraday Soc. **60,** 1769 (1964).
2. Benson, J. Chem. Phys. **34,** 521 (1961).

Ratios of Rate Constants (Isopropoxy Radicals)

Reaction	Notes	$E_1 - E_2$	$\log_{10}A_1/A_2$	k_1/k_2	Temperature range	Radical source	Reference
		(*kcal mole*$^{-1}$)			°*C*		
(1) $i\text{-}C_3H_7O = CH_3CHO + CH_3$ (2) $i\text{-}C_3H_7O + (CH_3)_2CHOOCC_2H_5 = i\text{-}C_3H_7OH + R$		<6			28	$C_2H_5COOCH(CH_3)_2$ P	1
(1) $i\text{-}C_3H_7O = CH_3CHO + CH_3$ (2) $i\text{-}C_3H_7O + NO = CH_3COCH_3 + HNO$		16			175–200	$(CH_3)_2CHONO$ T	2
(1) $i\text{-}C_3H_7O + CH_3CHO = i\text{-}C_3H_7OH + CH_3CO$ (2) $i\text{-}C_3H_7O + (i\text{-}C_3H_7O)_2 = i\text{-}C_3H_7OH + R$				27 ± 4	26	$(i\text{-}C_3H_7O)_2$ P	3

References

1. Wijnen, J. Am. Chem. Soc. **82,** 1847 (1960).
2. Ferguson and Phillips, J. Chem. Soc. 4416 (1965).
3. McMillan, J. Am. Chem. Soc. **83,** 3018 (1961).

Review

1. Gray and Williams, Chem. Rev. **59,** 239 (1959).

Metathetical Reactions of Butyl Radicals

Reactants	Notes	E	$\log_{10}A$	Temperature range	Radical source		Reference
		HYDROGEN ATOM TRANSFER					
(i) n-butyl radicals	(a)	*(kcal mole^{-1})*	*(cm^3 mole^{-1} sec^{-1})*	°C			
n-C_4H_9CHO		5.4	10.9	61–229	n-C_4H_9CHO	P	1
$HCOOCH_2CH_2CH_2CH_3$		5.3	10.2	75–186	CH_3COCH_3	P	2
(ii) sec-butyl radicals	(a)						
$CH_3CH_2CH(CH_3)CHO$		4.9	10.7	25–349	$CH_3CH_2CH(CH_3)CHO$	P	3
(iii) iso-butyl radicals	(a)						
i-C_4**H**$_9$CHO		12.7 ± 0.2	12.62 ± 0.05	178–279	i-C_4H_9CHO	P	4
i-C_4H_9**CHO**		6.5 ± 0.1	11.71 ± 0.07	117–230	i-C_4H_9CHO	P	4
$(i$-$C_4H_9)_2CO$		7.6	11.4	78–194	$(i$-$C_4H_9)_2CO$	P	5
	(c)	6.8 ± 0.2	11.06 ± 0.09				4
(iv) t-butyl radicals	(b)						
(C**H**$_3$)$_3$CCHO		10.0	11.2	240–386	$(CH_3)_3CCHO$	P	6
(CH$_3$)$_3$CC**H**O	(d)	4.3	9.8	60–386	$(CH_3)_3CCHO$	P	6

Ratios of Rate Constants (t-Butyl Radical)

Reaction	Notes	E_1-E_2	$\log_{10}A_1/A_2$	k_1/k_2	Temperature range	Radical source		Reference
		(kcal mole^{-1})			°C			
(1) t-$C_4H_9 + HBr = C_4H_{10} + Br$ (2) t-$C_4H_9 + Br_2 = C_4H_9Br + Br$		8.0	5.11		40–85	$(CH_3)_3CH/Br_2$	T	7, 8, 9
(1) t-$C_4H_9 + HI = C_4H_{10} + I$ (2) t-$C_4H_9 + I_2 = C_4H_9I + I$				0.226 0.234 0.251	526 552 583	$(CH_3)_3CH/I_2$	T	8

Notes

(a) The rate constants are based on log k (cm^3 mole^{-1} sec^{-1}) $= 10^{14}$ for the combination of n-, *sec*-, and *iso*-butyl radicals.
(b) The rate constants are based on log k (cm^3 mole^{-1} sec^{-1}) $= 10^{12.5}$ for the combination of t-butyl radicals.
(c) Recalculation of data from reference 5.
(d) This value of the activation energy is probably low.

References

1. Kerr and Trotman-Dickenson, J. Chem. Soc. 1602 (1960).
2. Thynne, Trans. Faraday Soc. **58,** 1533 (1962).
3. Gruver and Calvert, J. Am. Chem. Soc. **78,** 5208 (1956).
4. Metcalfe and Trotman-Dickenson, J. Chem. Soc. 5072 (1960).
5. Kraus and Calvert, J. Am. Chem. Soc. **79,** 5921 (1957).
6. Birrell and Trotman-Dickenson, J. Chem. Soc. 4218 (1960).
7. Eckstein, Scheraga, and Van Artsdalen, J. Phys. Chem. **22,** 28 (1954).
8. Teranishi and Benson, J. Am. Chem. Soc. **85,** 2887 (1963).
9. Benson and Buss, J. Chem. Phys. **28,** 301 (1958).

Metathetical Reactions of *t*-Butoxy Radicals

Reactants	Notes	E	$\log_{10}A$	Temperature range	Radical source		Reference
HYDROGEN ATOM TRANSFER							
		(*kcal mole*$^{-1}$)	(*cm*^{3} *mole*$^{-1}$ *sec*$^{-1}$)	°*C*			
$(CH_3)_3CH$		4.0	10.8	25–79	D.T.B.P.	P	4

Ratios of Rate Constants (*t*-Butoxy Radicals)

Reaction	Notes	$E_1 - E_2$	$\log_{10}A_1/A_2$	k_1/k_2	Temperature range	Radical source		Reference
		(*kcal mole*$^{-1}$)			°*C*			
(1) $(CH_3)_3CO + CH_2O = (CH_3)_3COH + HCO$ (2) $(CH_3)_3CO = CH_3 + CH_3COCH_3$				$(3.8 \pm 0.8) \times 10^5$ cm^3 mole^{-1}	135	D.T.B.P.	T	1
(1) $(CH_3)_3CO + ((CH_3)_3CO)_2 = (CH_3)_3COH + R$ (2) $(CH_3)_3CO = CH_3 + CH_3COCH_3$		-3			25–79	D.T.B.P.	P	2
(1) $(CH_3)_3CO + (CH_2)_2NH = (CH_3)_3COH + R$ (2) $(CH_3)_3CO = CH_3 + CH_3COCH_3$		-12 ± 2			129–154	D.T.B.P.	P	3

References

1. Hoare and Wellington, 8th Int. Comb. Symp., p. 472 (Williams and Wilkins 1962).
2. McMillan and Wijnen, Can. J. Chem. **36,** 1227 (1958).
3. Brinton and Volman, J. Chem. Phys. **20,** 25 (1952).
4. McMillan, J. Am. Chem. Soc. **82,** 2422 (1960).

Review

1. Gray and Williams, Chem. Rev. **59,** 239 (1959).

Metathetical Reactions of Peracid Radicals

Reactants	Notes	E	log₁₀A	Temperature range	Radical source		Reference
		HYDROGEN ATOM TRANSFER					
(i) Peracetic Radicals		*(kcal mole⁻¹)*	*(cm³ mole⁻¹ sec⁻¹)*	°C			
CH_3CHO		$k=(8.05\pm2.40)\times10^6$		20	CH_3CHO/O_2	P	1
(ii) Perpropionic Radicals							
C_2H_5CHO		$k=(4.35\pm0.91)\times10^7$		22	C_2H_5CHO/O_2	P	1

Ratio of Rate Constants (Peracid Radicals)

Reaction	Notes	E_1-E_2	$\log_{10}A_1/A_2$	k_1/k_2	Temperature range	Radical source		Reference
(i) Peracetic Radicals		*(kcal mole⁻¹)*			°C			
(1) $CH_3CO_3+CH_3CHO = CH_3CO_3H+CH_3CO$ (2) $2CH_3CO_3 = (CH_3CO)_2O_2+O_2$		$E_1-\frac{1}{2}E_2=7.2\pm1.0$			20–30	CH_3CHO/O_2	P	2
(ii) Perpropionic Radicals								
(1) $C_2H_5CO_3+C_2H_5CHO = C_2H_5CO_3H+C_2H_5CO$ (2) $2C_2H_5CO_3 = (C_2H_5CO)_2O_2+O_2$		$E_1-\frac{1}{2}E_2=6.75\pm0.5$			20–47	C_2H_5CHO/O_2	P	3

References

1. McDowell and Sharples, Can. J. Chem. **36,** 268 (1958).
2. McDowell and Sharples, Can. J. Chem. **36,** 251 (1958).
3. McDowell and Sharples, Can. J. Chem. **36,** 258 (1958).

Metathetical Reactions of Peroxy Radicals

Reactants	Notes	E	$\log_{10}A$	Temperature range	Radical source		Reference
HYDROGEN ATOM TRANSFER							
(i) Isobutyl peroxy radicals		(*kcal mole*$^{-1}$)	(*cm*^{3} *mole*$^{-1}$ *sec*$^{-1}$)	°C			
$(CH_3)_3CH$	(a) (b)	16.0	$4\times10^{-2}Z$	327–427	$(CH_3)_3CH/O_2$	$-H$	1
(ii) Cyclohexenyl peroxy radicals							
cyclohexene	(a) (b)	7.0	$6\times10^{-7}Z$	152–352	C_6H_{10}/O_2	$-H$	1
(iii) Isopropyl benzene peroxy radicals							
$C_6H_5CH(CH_3)_2$	(a) (b)	7.0	$2\times10^{-6}Z$	252–357	$C_6H_5CH(CH_3)_2$	$-H$	1

Notes

(a) The peroxy radical is the radical formed by oxygen addition to any hydrocarbon radical produced in the primary act.

(b) "Z" is the collision number.

Reference

1. Burgess and Robb, Trans. Faraday Soc. **54**, 1015 (1958).

Metathetical Reactions of Phenyl Radicals

Reactants	Notes	E	$\log_{10}A$ [(a)]	Tempera-ture range	Radical source		Reference
HYDROGEN ATOM TRANSFER							
		(kcal mole^{-1})	*(cm^3 mole^{-1} sec^{-1})*	*°C*			
H_2		6.5	10.97	180–350	$(C_6H_5)_2Hg$	P	1
CH_4		7.5	11.19	180–350	$(C_6H_5)_2Hg$	P	1
		11.1	11.9	277–407	$CH_3COC_6H_5$	P	2
cyclo-C_3H_6		8.5	11.4	310–407	$CH_3COC_6H_5$	P	2
i-C_4H_{10}		6.7	11.8	277–407	$CH_3COC_6H_5$	P	2
$CH_3COC_6H_5$		6.2	11.6	277–407	$CH_3COC_6H_5$	P	2
CF_3H		5.2	10.17	180–350	$(C_6H_5)_2Hg$	P	1
GROUP TRANSFER REACTION							
$C_6H_5 + C_6H_5COCH_3 = C_6H_5C_6H_5 + CH_3CO$		6.2	9.6	277–407	$CH_3COC_6H_5$	P	2

Note

(a) These values are based on log k (cm^3 mole^{-1} sec^{-1}) $= 10^{14}$ for the combination of phenyl radicals.

References

1. Fielding and Pritchard, J. Phys. Chem. **66,** 821 (1962).
2. Duncan and Trotman-Dickenson, J. Chem. Soc. 4672 (1962).

247-168 O-67—7

Ratios of Rate Constants (Tolyl Radicals)

Reactions	Notes	$E_1 - E_2$	$\log_{10}A_1/A_2$	k_1/k_2	Temperature range	Radical source		Reference
		(kcal mole⁻¹)			°C			
(1) $CH_3C_6H_4 + C_6H_4(CH_3)_2 = CH_3C_6H_5 + CH_3C_6H_4CH_2$ (2) $CH_3C_6H_4 + D_2 = CH_3C_6H_4D + D$	(a)			10.7	700	$(CH_3)_2C_6H_4/D_2$	T	1
(1) p-$CH_3C_6H_4 + C_6H_4(CH_3)_2 = CH_3C_6H_5 + CH_3C_6H_4CH_2$ (2) p-$CH_3C_6H_4 + D_2 = CH_3C_6H_4D + D$	(b)			24.6	484	p-$(CH_3)_2C_6H_4/D_2$	T	2

Notes

(a) No distinction was made between the *o*, *m*, and *p* xylenes.
(b) There appears to be a misprint in the original paper. The numbering of the reactions has been reversed.

References

1. Burr and Strong, J. Am. Chem. Soc. **86,** 5065 (1964).
2. Burr and Strong, J. Chem. Phys. **43,** 1432 (1965).

Hydroxyl Radicals

Reactants	Notes	E	$\log_{10}A$	Temperature range	Radical source	Reference
			HYDROGEN ATOM TRANSFER			
Hydrogen		(*kcal mole*$^{-1}$)	(*cm*^{3} *mole*$^{-1}$ *sec*$^{-1}$)	°C		
H_2		11.0	14.52	105–216	H_2O/ discharge	1
			$k=2.0\times10^{10}$	520	H_2/O_2 ignition	2
	(a)	10.0	14.1			3
		10.0	14.40		H_2O_2 flames	4
			$k=4.3\times10^{9}$	37	NO_2/H reaction	5
	(b)	5.9 ± 1.0	13.80 ± 0.7	27–1700		6
			$k=(3.5\pm0.3)\times10^{9}$	27	H_2/ discharge	7
	(b) (c)	$5.0(5.3)\pm0.6$	13.13(13.33)	27–799		8
	(b) (c)	$5.3(5.5)\pm0.6$	13.33(13.49)	27–799		9
			$k=1.1\times10^{12}$	642	H_2/O_2 flame	10
			$k=(3.9\pm0.2)\times10^{9}$	27	NO_2/H reaction	11
	(b)	5.2	13.36	27–1677		11
		6.4	14.17	687–807	H_2/O_2 ignition	12
Alkanes						
CH_4		8.3	14.38		H_2O/ discharge	13
		9.0	14.54	1027–1527	CH_4/O_2 flame	14
			$k=2\times10^{13}$	1377–1567	CH_4/O_2 flame	15
		6.5	14.15	930–1530	CH_4/O_2 flame	16
	(d)	7.9	14.36			17
C_2H_2			$k=2\times10^{12}$	1400–1700	C_2H_2/O_2 flame	18
		7.3	14.44	50–237	H_2O/ discharge	19
C_2H_4			$k=1\times10^{13}$	977–1127	C_2H_4/O_2 flame	20
		6.4	14.60	77–178	H_2O/ discharge	19
C_2H_6		5.5	14.11	65–228	H_2O/ discharge	19
			$k=2.5\times10^{13}$	1147–1337	$C_2H_6/H_2/O_2$ flame	34
	(e)		$k=2.1\times10^{13}$	520	H_2/O_2 ignition	21
			$k=5\times10^{12}$	1027–1227	C_2H_6/O_2 flame	20
C_3H_8	(e)		$k=4.3\times10^{13}$	520	H_2/O_2 ignition	21
n-C_4H_{10}			$k=5.8\times10^{13}$	520	H_2/O_2 ignition	21
i-C_4H_{10}			$k=3.2\times10^{13}$	520	H_2/O_2 ignition	21
Aldehydes						
HCHO		0.9	14.11	73–216	H_2O/ discharge	22
	(b)	13.0	15.7	73–1339		20
CH_3CHO		4.0	13.53	53–209	H_2O/ discharge	22
Acid						
HNO_3			$k=1.0\times10^{11}$	27	HNO_3 flash photolysis	23
Halogenated Alkane						
CH_3Br			$k=1.5\times10^{13}$	1527–1727	CH_4/O_2 flame	24

Hydroxyl Radicals – Continued

Reactants	Notes	E (kcal mole^{-1})	$\log_{10}A$ (cm^3 mole^{-1} sec^{-1})	Temperature range °C	Radical source	Reference
			OXYGEN ATOM TRANSFER			
CO	(g)	7.0	13.08	70–203	H_2O/ discharge	1
	(a)	5.7	12.46			3
		$k=9\times10^{11}$		1677	CH_4/O_2 flame	15
	(d)	5.7	12.46			17
	(b)	7.7	12.85	127–1727		20
		4.0	12	1107–1447	flame study.	25
	(b)	6.2 ± 0.6	12.6 ± 0.3	107–1677		8
	(b) (c)	$0.5(0.8)\pm0.6$	$11.5(11.7)\pm0.3$	200–800		8
		$k=(1.15\pm0.5)\times10^{11}$		27	NO_2/H reaction	11
	(b)	0.6	11.49	27–1677		11
			MISCELLANEOUS REACTIONS			
$OH+F_2=HF+F+O$		18.0	15.3		F_2/H_2O flames	26
		18.0	13.85	497–557	F_2/H_2O ignition	26

Hydroxyl Radicals (Rate Constant Ratios)

Reaction	Notes	E_1-E_2 (kcal mole^{-1})	$\log_{10}A_1/A_2$	k_1/k_2	Temperature range °C	Radical source	Reference
(1) $C_2H_6+OH=C_2H_5+H_2O$ (2) $H_2+OH=H+H_2O$	(f)			12	540	H_2/O_2 ignigion	27
(1) $C_3H_8+OH=C_3H_7+H_2O$ (2) $H_2+OH=H+H_2O$	(f)			27	520	H_2/O_2 ignition	27
(1) n-$C_4H_{10}+OH=C_4H_9+H_2O$ (2) $H_2+OH=H+H_2O$	(f)			36	520	H_2/O_2 ignition	27
(1) i-$C_4H_{10}+OH=C_4H_9+H_2O$ (2) $H_2+OH=H+H_2O$	(f)			20	520	H_2/O_2 ignition	27
(1) $HCHO+OH=HCO+H_2O$ (2) $H_2+OH=H+H_2O$	(f)			42	540	H_2/O_2 ignition	27
(1) $(C_2H_5)_4Si+OH$ $=(C_2H_5)_3Si.C_2H_4+H_2O$ (2) $H_2+OH=H+H_2O$	(f)			74	520	H_2/O_2 ignition	27
(1) $H_2O_2+OH=HO_2+H_2O$ (2) $H_2+OH=H_2O+H$				4.8 to 5.7	447	H_2/O_2 ignition	28
				7.1	500	H_2/O_2 ignition	29
				5.5	440	H_2/O_2 ignition	30
				4.3 ± 0.3	440	H_2/O_2 pyrolysis	27
				4.7	500	H_2 combustion	27

Hydroxyl Radicals (Rate Constant Ratios)—Continued

Reaction	Notes	E_1-E_2	$\log_{10}A_1/A_2$	k_1/k_2	Temperature range	Radical source	Reference
		(kcal mole⁻¹)			°C		
(1) $H_2+OH=H+H_2O$							
(2) $CO+OH=CO_2+H$		4.0 ± 0.3	1.49 ± 0.7		200–350	H_2O photolysis	31
				5.0	520	H_2/O_2 ignition	27
				3.3		CO/H_2 combustion	27
	(b)	5.16	1.98		500–1002		27
	(b)	4.6 ± 0.3	1.87		27–1002		11
(1) $D_2+OH=D+HDO$							
(2) $CO+OH=CO_2+H$		6.4 ± 0.3	2.20 ± 0.09		200–300	H_2O photolysis	31
(1) $CH_4+OH=CH_3+H_2O$							
(2) $CO+OH=CO_2+H$		7.3	2.28		400–650	H_2O_2 pyrolysis	32
(1) $HCHO+OH=HCO+H_2O$				33	525	H_2O_2 pyrolysis	32
(2) $CH_4+OH=CH_3+H_2O$				27	600	H_2O_2 pyrolysis	32
				22	650	H_2O_2 pyrolysis	32
				33	500	CH_4 combustion	33

Notes

(a) Used at flame temperatures.
(b) Critical survey of literature data.
(c) ΔH_f (OH) = 9.33 (10.0) kcal/mole.
(d) This value was used by the authors in the region 1000°–1500° but its origin was not stated.
(e) Measured relative to $OH+H_2=H_2O+H$, for which $k=1.6\times10^9$ at 520 °C.
(f) Calculated on the assumption that oxygen atom reactions could be neglected.
(g) The products of this reaction are CO_2+H.

References

1. Avramenko and Lorentso, Zhur. Fiz. Khim. **24,** 207 (1950).
2. Baldwin, Trans. Faraday Soc. **52,** 1344 (1956).
3. Kondratiev, 7th. Int. Comb. Symp., p. 41 (Butterworths, London, 1959).
4. Fenimore and Jones, J. Phys. Chem. **65,** 993 (1961).
5. Del Greco and Kaufman, Disc. Faraday Soc. **33,** 128 (1962).
6. Kaufman and Del Greco, 9th. Int. Comb. Symp., p. 659 (Academic Press, N.Y., 1963).
7. Wise, Ablow, Sancier, and Wood, Project Squid, Semi Annual Report, p. 59 (April, 1964).
8. Dixon-Lewis, Sutton, and Williams, Trans. Faraday Soc. **61,** 255 (1965).
9. Dixon-Lewis, Sutton, and Williams, J. Chem. Soc. 5724 (1965).
10. Dixon-Lewis, Sutton and Williams, 10th. Int. Comb. Symp. Comb. Inst., p. 495 (Pittsburgh, 1965).
11. Dixon-Lewis, Wilson, and Westenberg, J. Chem. Phys. **44,** 2877 (1966).
12. Skinner and Ringrose, J. Chem. Phys. **42,** 2190 (1965).
13. Avramenko and Kolesnikova, "Advances in photochemistry," p. 25 (Interscience Publishers, N.Y., 1964).
14. Fenimore and Jones, J. Phys. Chem. **65,** 2200 (1961).
15. Westenberg and Fristom, J. Phys. Chem. **65,** 591 (1961).
16. Fristrom, 9th. Int. Comb. Symp., p. 560 (Academic Press N.Y., 1963).
17. Intezarova, Kondratiev, and Mukhoyan, Kinetika i Kataliz **5,** 585 (1964).
18. Fenimore and Jones, J. Chem. Phys. **41,** 1887 (1964).
19. Avramenko and Lorentso, Dokl. Akad. Nauk. S.S.S.R. **67,** 867 (1949).
20. Westenberg and Fristrom, 10th. Int. Comb. Symp. Comb. Inst., p. 473 (Pittsburgh, 1965).
21. Baldwin and Walker, Trans. Faraday Soc. **60,** 1236 (1964).
22. Avramenko and Lorentso, Dokl. Akad. Nauk. S.S.S.R. **69,** 205 (1949).
23. Husain and Norrish, Proc. Roy. Soc. **273A,** 165 (1963).
24. Wilson, 10th. Int. Comb. Symp. Comb. Inst., p. 47 (Pittsburgh, 1965).
25. Jost, Schecker, and Wagner, Z. Phys. Chem. **45,** 56 (1965).
26. Nosova, Lovachev, and Vedeneev, Comb. and Flame **8,** 163 (1964).
27. Baldwin, Jackson, Walker, and Webster, 10th. Int. Comb. Symp. Comb. Inst., p. 473 (Pittsburgh, 1965).
28. Forst and Giguere, J. Phys. Chem. **62,** 340 (1958).
29. Baldwin and Mayor, Trans. Faraday Soc. **56,** 103 (1960).
30. Baldwin and Doran, Trans. Faraday Soc. **57,** 1578 (1961).
31. Ung and Back, Can. J. Chem. **42,** 753 (1964).
32. Hoare, Nature **194,** 283 (1962).
33. Blundell, Cook, Hoare, and Milne, 10th. Int. Comb. Symp. Comb. Inst., p. 445 (Pittsburgh, 1965).
34. Fenimore and Jones, 9th. Int. Comb. Symp., p. 560 (Academic Press, N.Y., 1963).

Metathetical Reactions of Hydroperoxyl Radicals

Reactants	Notes	E	$\log_{10}A$	Temperature range	Radical source	Reference
		HYDROGEN ATOM TRANSFER				
		(kcal mole⁻¹)	*(cm³ mole⁻¹ sec⁻¹)*	°C		
H_2		24.0	11.08		H_2/O_2 ignition	1, 2
			$k=1.1\times10^7$	500	H_2/O_2 ignition	3
		14.8 ± 2.2		617–1007	H_2/O_2 ignition	4
			$k=1.3\times10^6$	500		7
		34.6	16.51	687–807		9
H_2O	(a)	8.0	8.1	600–615	H_2/O_2 ignition	1, 8
	(b)	30.0	13.26	600–615	H_2/O_2 ignition	2

Ratios of Rate Constants (Hydroperoxyl Radicals)

Reactions	Notes	E_1-E_2	$\log_{10}A_1/A_2$	k_1/k_2	Temperature range	Radical source	Reference
		(kcal mole⁻¹)			°C		
(1) $CO+HO_2=CO_2+OH$ (2) $H_2+HO_2=H+H_2O_2$				9.5 ± 2	500	$H_2/CO/O_2$ ignition	5
(1) $HCHO+HO_2$ $=HCO+H_2O_2$ (2) $CO+HO_2=CO_2+OH$				340	525	CH_4/O_2 T	6

Notes

(a) These values must be rejected on thermochemical grounds.
(b) Is a recalculation of data from (a).

References

1. Voevodsky, 7th. Int. Comb. Symp., p. 34 (Butterworths, London, 1959).
2. Kondratiev, Dokl. Akad. Nauk. S.S.S.R. **137,** 120 (1961).
3. Baldwin and Mayor, Trans. Faraday Soc. **56,** 103 (1960).
4. Miyama and Takeyama, J. Chem. Phys. **41,** 2287 (1964).
5. Baldwin, Jackson, Walker, and Webster, 10th Int. Comb. Symp. Comb. Inst., p. 423 (Pittsburgh, 1965).
6. Blundell, Cook, Hoare, and Milne, 10th. Int. Comb. Symp. Comb. Inst., p. 445 (Pittsburgh, 1965).
7. Dixon-Lewis and Williams, Nature **196,** 1309 (1962).
8. Poltorak and Voevodsky, Zhur. Fiz. Khim. **24,** 299 (1950).
9. Skinner and Ringrose, J. Chem. Phys. **42,** 2190 (1965).

Metathetical Reactions of Imino Radicals

Reactants	Notes	E		log₁₀A	Temperature range	Radical source		Reference
			(kcal mole^{-1})	*(cm^3 mole^{-1} sec^{-1})*	°C			
HYDROGEN ATOM TRANSFER								
HNCO	(a)	3.6			−31–200	HNCO	P	1

Note

(a) The products of this reaction are NH_2 and NCO.

Reference

1. Mui and Back, Can. J. Chem. **41,** 826 (1963).

Metathetical Reactions of Amino Radicals

Reactants	Notes	E	$\log_{10}A$	Temperature range	Radical source	References
		(*kcal mole*$^{-1}$)	(*cm*^{3} *mole*$^{-1}$ *sec*$^{-1}$)	°C		
$NH_2+N_2H_4$ $=NH_3+N_2H_3$		$k=7.9\times10^{10}$		25		1
		17	13.5	830–1130	N_2H_4 S.T.	4
$NH_2+O_2=NH+HO_2$		42.5 ± 1.2		1277–2027	NH_3/O_2 S.T.	2

Metathetieal Reactions of Amino Radicals Ratios of Rate Constants

Reactants	Notes	E_1-E_2	$\log_{10}A_1/A_2$	k_1/k_2	Temperature range	Radical source	Reference
		(*kcal mole*$^{-1}$)			°C		
(1) $NH_2+(CH_3)_2N\cdot NH_2$ $=NH_3+(CH_3)_2N\cdot NH$ (2) $NH_2+(CH_3)_2N\cdot NH_2$ $=NH_3+(CH_3)(CH_2)N\cdot NH_2$				6.6×10^{-3}	250	$(CH_3)_2N.NH_2$ T	3

References

1. Diesen, J. Chem. Phys. **39,** 2121 (1963).
2. Takeyama and Miyama, J. Chem. Phys. **42,** 3737 (1965).
3. Cordes, J. Phys. Chem. **65,** 1473 (1961).
4. Michel and Wagner, 10th Int. Comb. Symp. Comb. Inst., p. 353 (Pittsburgh, 1965).

Metathetical Reactions of Difluoroamino Radicals

Reactions	Notes	E	$\log_{10}A$	Temperature range	Radical source	Reference
HYDROGEN ATOM TRANSFER						
Alkanes		(*kcal mole*$^{-1}$)	(*cm*^{3} *mole*$^{-1}$ *sec*$^{-1}$)	°C		
n-C_4H_{10}		22.20 ± 0.08	11.83 ± 0.04	180–282	N_2F_4/n-C_4H_{10} T	1
i-C_4H_{10}		18.49 ± 0.10	10.49 ± 0.04	155–282	N_2F_4/i-C_4H_{10} T	1
cyclo-C_5H_{10}		19.91 ± 0.11	10.93 ± 0.05	180–282	N_2F_4/cyclo-C_5H_{10} T	1
neo-C_5H_{12}		26.68 ± 0.07	13.22 ± 0.03	180–282	N_2F_4/neo-C_5H_{12} T	1
Ketone						
CH_3COCH_3		19.56 ± 0.11	10.71 ± 0.05	170–280	N_2F_4/CH_3COCH_3 T	2
FLUORINE ATOM TRANSFER						
F_2O		22.5 ± 0.7	14.01	120–170	N_2F_4/F_2O T	3

References

1. Grzechowiak, Kerr, and Trotman-Dickenson, Chem. Comm. 109 (1965).
2. Grzechowiak, Kerr, and Trotman-Dickenson, J. Chem. Soc. 5080 (1965).
3. Rubinstein, Sicre, and Schumacher, Z. Phys. Chem. **43,** 64 (1964).

Metathetical Reactions of Nitrate Radicals

Reactions	Notes	E	$\log_{10} A$	Temperature range	Radical source	Reference
		(kcal mole⁻¹)	*(cm³ mole⁻¹ sec⁻¹)*	°C		
$NO_3+NO=2NO_2$			$k=6\times10^{12}$	27		1
		1.4±2.5	13.8		N_2O_5 S.T.	2
			$k=2.7\times10^{12}$	27	NO_2/O_3 P	3
		1.7	12.62	200–550	NO_2 T	4
			$k=1\times10^{14}$	25	NO_2 F.P.	5
$NO_3+NO_2=NO_2+NO+O_2$		3.9±1.0	11.22	27–547	N_2O_5 S.T.	1, 2
		3.2±1.0	11.07±0.47	200–550	NO_2 T	4
$NO_3+NOCl=NO_2+NO_2Cl$	(a)		$k=7.0\times10^{7}$	40	$NOCl/O_3/N_2O_5$ T	6
			$k=2.3\times10^{7}$	40		2

Ratios of Rate Constants

Reactions	Notes	E_1-E_2	$\log_{10} A_1/A_2$	k_1/k_2	Temperature range	Radical source	Reference
		(kcal mole⁻¹)			°C		
(1) $NO_3+NO=2NO_2$ (2) $NO_3+NO_2=NO_2+NO+O_2$				60	434	NO_2 T	7
	(b)	1.4	2.2		20–30	NO/N_2O_5 T	8, 9
	(c)	2.3	3.2		20–30	NO/N_2O_5 T	8, 9

Notes

(a) The A factor was assumed, only the rate constant was determined.
(b) At 400 mm total pressure.
(c) At 57 mm total pressure.

References

1. Davidson and Schott, J. Chem. Phys. **27,** 317 (1957).
2. Schott and Davidson, J. Am. Chem. Soc. **80,** 1841 (1958).
3. Ford, Doyle, and Endow, J. Chem. Phys. **32,** 1256 (1960).
4. Ashmore and Burnett, Trans. Faraday Soc. **58,** 253 (1962).
5. Husain and Norrish, Proc. Roy. Soc. **273A,** 165 (1963).
6. Johnston and Leighton, J. Am. Chem. Soc. **75,** 3612 (1953).
7. Ashmore and Levitt, Research **9,** S25 (1956).
8. Hisatsune, Crawford, and Ogg, J. Am. Chem. Soc. **79,** 4648 (1957).
9. Hisatsune, McHale, Nightingale, Rotenberg, and Crawford, J. Chem. Phys. **23,** 2467 (1955).

Metathetical Reactions of Thiyl Radicals

Reactant	Note	E	$\log_{10} A$	Tempera-ture range	Radical source	References
HYDROGEN ATOM TRANSFER						
		(kcal mole⁻¹)	*(cm³ mole⁻¹ sec⁻¹)*	°C		
CH_3OCH_3	(a)	6.8	11	360–440	CH_3OCH_3/H_2S T	1, 2

Notes

(a) For further data on systems containing HS radicals, see reference 3.

References

1. Imai and Toyama, Bull. Chem. Soc. Japan **34,** 328 (1961).
2. Anderson and Benson, J. Chem. Phys. **39,** 1677 (1963).
3. Imai, Yoshida, and Toyama, Bull. Chem. Soc. Japan **35,** 752 (1962).

Reactions of Chloromonoxy Radicals

Reactions	Notes	E	$\log_{10} A$	Temperature range	Radical source	Reference
		(kcal mole⁻¹)	*(cm³ mole⁻¹ sec⁻¹)*	°C		
$ClO + Cl_2O = ClO_2 + Cl_2$		$k = 10^8$			Cl_2O F.P.	1
$ClO + Cl_2O = Cl + O_2 + Cl_2$		$k = 5.3 \times 10^7$			Cl_2O F.P.	1
$ClO + NO_3Cl = NO_2 + Cl_2 + O_2$		~17		90–130	NO_3Cl T	2

Ratios of Rate Constants (Chloromonoxy Radicals)

Reactions	Notes	$E_1 - E_2$	$\log_{10} A_1/A_2$	k_1/k_2	Temperature range	Radical source	Reference
		(kcal mole⁻¹)			°C		
(1) $ClO + C_3H_8 = HOCl + CH_3CHCH_3$ (2) $ClO + C_3H_8 = HOCl + CH_3CH_2CH_2$				7.2 ± 0.5	100	C_3H_8/Cl_2O T	3

References

1. Edgecombe, Norrish, and Thrush, Proc. Roy. Soc. **243A**, 24 (1957).
2. Cafferata, Sicre, and Schumacher, Z. Phys. Chem. **29**, 188 (1961).
3. Phillips and Shaw, Proc. Chem. Soc. 294 (1962).

Reactions of Borine Radicals

Reactants	Notes	E	$\log_{10} A$	Temperature range	Radical source	Reference
		(*kcal mole*$^{-1}$)	(*cm*^{3} *mole*$^{-1}$ *sec*$^{-1}$)	°C		
$BH_3 + B_2H_6 = B_3H_7 + H_2$		11.5	11.06			1, 9
$BH_3 + B_2D_6 = BH_3BD_3 + BD_3$		6.0 7.8	14.2 13.45	24–44	B_2H_6/B_2D_6. T	4, 5, 6, 3 1
$BH_3 + BH_3CO = B_2H_6 + CO$		7.0	11.4	0–30	BH_3CO T	7, 4, 3
$BH_3 + H_2O = BH_2OH + H_2$		6	11.28	51	B_2H_6/H_2O T	8, 9
$BH_3 + HD = BH_2D + H_2$		7	11.6			9

Ratios of Rate Constants Involving Borine Radicals

Reaction	Notes	$E_1 - E_2$	$\log_{10} A_1/A_2$	k_1/k_2	Temperature range	Radical source	Reference
		(*kcal mole*$^{-1}$)			°C		
(1) $BH_3 + B_2D_6 = BD_3BH_3 + BD_3$ (2) $BH_3 + D_2 = BH_2D + HD$				0.25	55	B_2H_6/D_2 T	2, 3
(1) $BH_3 + O_2 = BH_2OH + O$ (2) $BH_3 + O_2 + M = HBO_2 + H_2 + M$		2.0			150–200	B_2H_6/O_2 T	1

References

1. Roth and Bauer, 5th Int. Comb. Symp., p. 710 (Reinhold, N.Y., 1955).
2. Marcus, J. Chem. Phys. **23,** 1107 (1955).
3. Garabedian and Benson, J. Am. Chem. Soc. **86,** 176 (1964).
4. Bauer, Shepp, and McCoy, J. Am. Chem. Soc. **75,** 1003 (1953).
5. Trotman-Dickenson, "Gas Kinetics," p. 237 et seq. (Butterworths, London, 1955).
6. Maybury and Koski, J. Chem. Phys. **21,** 742 (1953).
7. Burg, J. Am. Chem. Soc. **74,** 3482 (1952).
8. Weiss and Shapiro, J. Am. Chem. Soc. **75,** 1221 (1953).
9. Bauer, J. Am. Chem. Soc. **78,** 5775 (1956).

Metathetical Reactions of F_3SO and FSO_3 Radicals

Reactions	Notes	E	$\log_{10} A$	Temperature range	Radical source		Reference
		(*kcal mole*$^{-1}$)	(*cm*^{3} *mole*$^{-1}$ *sec*$^{-1}$)	°C			
$F_3SO+F_2=F_4SO+F$		10.0 ± 2		5–20	F_2/F_2SO	P	1
$FSO_3+F_2=F_2SO_3+F$		14.7 ± 1.0	8.68	230–250	$F_2/F_2S_2O_6$	T	2

References

1. Castellano and Schumacher, Z. Phys. Chem. N.F. **40**, 51 (1964).

2. Castellano and Schumacher, Z. Phys. Chem. N.F. **44**, 57 (1965).

Radical Disproportionation Reactions

The reactions are classified in the same order as the tables of radical reactions. Thus the first set of reactions are those involving atoms, followed by reactions of radicals containing one carbon atom, etc.

Reactions	Notes	*E*	$\log_{10} A$	$\log_{10} k$	Temperature range	Radical source	Reference
		(*kcal mole*$^{-1}$)	(*cm*^{3} *mole*$^{-1}$ *sec*$^{-1}$)	(*cm*^{3} *mole*$^{-1}$ *sec*$^{-1}$)	°*C*		
$H+OH=H_2+O$		5.8 ± 1.5	12.76 ± 1.0		25–2000		4
		7.4	12.74		687–807	H_2/O_2 S.T.	12
$H+HO_2=2OH$				14.86	25	H_2/O_2 −H	5
				13.84	500		6
$H+HNO=H_2+NO$				> 9.78	20	H_2/discharge	1
				> 10.48	−47	H_2/discharge	2
				12.78 ± 0.25	1300–1700	$H_2/O_2/N_2$ flame	3
$H+C_2F_4Br=C_2F_4+HBr$		11.5	16.3		855–1013	$H_2/O_2/C_2F_4Br_2$ S.T.	7
$Cl+C_2HCl_4=C_2HCl_3+Cl_2$				13.85	224	$CHCl{:}CCl_2/Cl_2$ P	25, 24
$Cl+C_2Cl_5=C_2Cl_4+Cl_2$		1.2	15.6				24
$Cl+COCl=CO+Cl_2$		0.8	14.6		25–55	CO/Cl_2 P	33, 24
	(a)	2.4	13.70		15–450		34
$Cl+Cl_3=2Cl_2$				⩽ 14.23	20	Cl_2/discharge	19, 20
$I+NOI=NO+I_2$				12.60	60	NO/I_2 F.P.	30
$2CN=C_2+N_2$		96			3177–4527	C_2N_2 S.T.	14, 15
$2C_2H_3Cl_2=C_2H_3Cl+C_2H_3Cl_3$		0.3	12.9		25–55	$CH_2{:}CHCl/Cl_2$ P	29
$2CHCl_2CHCl=CHCl{:}CHCl+CHCl_2CHCl_2$		0.5 ± 0.5	13.47 ± 0.3		30–65	*cis*-$CHCl{:}CHCl/Cl_2$ P	31
$2C_2Cl_5=C_2Cl_4+C_2Cl_6$		0.08	11.66		87–247	C_2Cl_4/Cl_2 P	32
$2CH_3CO_3=(CH_3CO)_2O_2+O_2$				13.95	20	CH_3CHO/O_2 P	27
$2C_2H_5CO_3=(C_2H_5CO)_2O_2+O_2$				13.43	22	CH_3CH_2CHO/O_2 P	28
$2OH=H_2+O_2$		48.6	12.85		687–807	H_2/O_2 S.T.	12
$2OH=H_2O+O$				12.18	37–107	H_2/discharge	10
	(b)			12.08	27	H_2/discharge	11
		1.0 ± 0.5	12.88 ± 0.3		25–2000		4
		3.8	14.87		687–807	H_2/O_2 S.T.	12
	(b)			12.19	27	NO_2/H reaction	13
$OH+HNO=H_2O+NO$ (or H_2+NO_2)				13.95	1300–1700	$H_2/O_2/NO$ flame	3
$2HO_2=H_2O_2+O_2$				12.25	room temp.		6
				13.81	25	H_2/O_2 −H	5
$2NH_2=NH_3+NH$				13.40	1627–2127	NH_2NH_2 S.T.	8
				11.66		NH_3 F.P.	9
$2N_2H_3=2NH_3+N_2$				⩾ 12.48	150	H_2/discharge	18

Radical Disproportionation Reactions—Continued

The reactions are classified in the same order as the tables of radical reactions. Thus the first set of reactions are those involving atoms, followed by reactions of radicals containing one carbon atom, etc.

Reactions	Notes	E	$\log_{10} A$	$\log_{10} k$	Temperature range	Radical source	Reference
		(*kcal mole*$^{-1}$)	(*cm*^{3} *mole*$^{-1}$ *sec*$^{-1}$)	(*cm*^{3} *mole*$^{-1}$ *sec*$^{-1}$)	°C		
$2HNO = H_2O + N_2O$				> 7.48	27	NO/H reaction	16
				~ 8.9	190	$(CH_3)_2CHNO$ T	17
$2NO_3 = 2NO_2 + O_2$		7.7 ± 1.0	12.42		280–830	N_2O_5 S.T.	26
$2ClO = Cl_2 + O_2$				10.38		Cl_2O F.P.	21
				10.93	20	Cl_2O F.P.	22, 23

Ratios of Rate Constants (Radical Disproportion Reactions)

Reactions	Notes	Rate constants ratios	Temperature range	Radical source	Reference
		cm^3, *mole. sec. units*	°C		
(1) $H + HO_2 = 2OH$ (2) $2HO_2 = H_2O_2 + O_2$		$k_1^2/k_2 = 5.1 \times 10^{14}$	500	H_2/O_2 ignition	35, 36
(1) $2HS = H_2 + S_2$ (2) $2HS = H_2S + S$		$k_1/k_2 = 0.15$	room temp.	H_2S P	37
(1) $2HNO = H_2O + N_2O$ (2) $2HNO = 2NO + H_2$		$k_1/k_2 = 8$	25	C_2H_5OH/NO H	38
(1) $C_2H_5 + C_5H_9O_2 = C_2H_4 + C_2H_5COOC_2H_5$ (2) $C_2H_5 + C_5H_9O_2 = C_2H_6 + C_5H_8O_2$		$k_1/k_2 = 0.1$	29	$C_2H_5COOC_2H_5$ P	39
(1) $2C_2H_5O = C_2H_5OH + CH_3CHO$ (2) $C_2H_5O = CH_3 + CH_2O$		$k_1/k_2^2 = 1.2 \times 10^{10}$	152	$C_2H_5COOC_2H_5$ P	40
		$k_1/k_2^2 = (3 \pm 1) \times 10^{12}$	30	$C_2H_5COOC_2H_5$ P	40
(1) $2(CH_3)_3CO = (CH_3)_3COH + (CH_3)_2\overline{CCH_2O}$ (2) $(CH_3)_3CO = CH_3COCH_3 + CH_3$		$k_1/k_2^2 \leq 3.0 \times 10^8$	25	$((CH_3)_3CO)_2$ P	41

Notes

(a) Review of literature data.

(b) Value based on E.S.R. measurements of the radical concentration.

References

1. Clyne and Thrush, Trans. Faraday Soc. **57,** 1305 (1961).
2. Clyne and Thrush, Disc. Faraday Soc. **33,** 139 (1962).
3. Bulewicz and Sugden, Proc. Roy. Soc. **277A,** 143 (1964).
4. Kaufman and Del Greco, 9th Int. Comb. Symp., p. 659 (Academic Press, N.Y., 1963).
5. Burgess and Robb, Chem. Soc. Special Publ. No. 9 167 (1958).
6. Dixon-Lewis and Williams, Nature **196,** 1309 (1962).
7. Skinner and Ringrose, J. Chem. Phys. **43,** 4129 (1965).
8. Diesen, J. Chem. Phys. **39,** 2121 (1963).
9. Salzman and Bair, J. Chem. Phys. **41,** 3654 (1964).
10. Del Greco and Kaufman, Disc. Faraday Soc. **33,** 128 (1962).
11. Westenberg and De Haas, J. Chem. Phys. **43,** 1550 (1965).
12. Skinner and Ringrose, J. Chem. Phys. **42,** 2190 (1965).
13. Dixon-Lewis, Wilson, and Westenberg, J. Chem. Phys. **44,** 2877 (1966).
14. Fairbairn, Proc. Roy. Soc. **267A,** 88 (1962).
15. Paterson and Greene, J. Chem. Phys. **36,** 1146 (1962).
16. Clyne, 10th Int. Comb. Symp., p. 311 (Comb. Inst., Pittsburgh, 1965).

17. Ferguson and Phillips, J. Chem. Soc. 4416 (1965).
18. Schiavello and Volpi, J. Chem. Phys. **37,** 1510 (1962).
19. Hutton and Wright, Trans. Faraday Soc. **61,** 78 (1965).
20. Hutton, Nature **203,** 835 (1964).
21. Edgecombe, Norrish, and Thrush, Proc. Roy. Soc. **243A,** 24 (1957).
22. Lipscomb, Norrish, and Porter, Nature **174,** 785 (1954).
23. Porter and Wright, Disc. Faraday Soc. **14,** 23 (1953).
24. Goldfinger, Jeunehomme, and Martens, J. Chem. Phys. **29,** 456 (1958).
25. Huybrechts, Meyers, and Verbecke, Trans. Faraday Soc. **58,** 1128 (1962).
26. Schott and Davidson, J. Am. Chem. Soc. **80,** 1841 (1958).
27. McDowell and Sharples, Can. J. Chem. **36,** 268 (1958).
28. McDowell and Sharples, Can. J. Chem. **36,** 1227 (1958).
29. Dainton, Lomax, and Weston, Trans. Faraday Soc. **58,** 308 (1962).
30. Ayscough, Cocker, Dainton, and Hirst, Trans. Faraday Soc. **58,** 295 (1962).
31. Dusoleil, Goldfinger, Mahieu-van der Auwera, Martens, and van der Auwera, Trans. Faraday Soc. **57,** 2197 (1961).
32. Burns and Dainton, Trans. Faraday Soc. **48,** 39 (1952).
33. Bodenstein, Brenschede, and Schumacher, Z. Phys. Chem. **40B,** 121 (1938).
34. Baldwin and Mayor, Trans. Faraday Soc. **56,** 103 (1960).
35. Baldwin and Mayor, Trans. Faraday Soc. **56,** 80 (1960).
36. Darwent and Roberts, Proc. Roy. Soc. **216A,** 344 (1953).
37. Knight and Gunning, Can. J. Chem. **39,** 2466 (1961).
38. Wijnen, J. Am. Chem. Soc. **82,** 3034 (1960).
39. Wijnen, J. Am. Chem. Soc. **80,** 2394 (1958).
40. McMillan and Wijnen, Can. J. Chem. **36,** 1227 (1958).

247-168 O-67—8

Disproportionation/Combination Ratios

Index

Disproportionation/Combination Ratios

The following convention is used throughout this table, e.g. for ethyl and *n*-propyl radicals, the possible reactions are:

$$C_2H_5 + n\text{-}C_3H_7 = C_5H_{12} \quad (1)$$

$$C_2H_5 + n\text{-}C_3H_7 = C_2H_6 + C_3H_6 \quad (2)$$

$$C_2H_5 + n\text{-}C_3H_7 = C_2H_4 + C_3H_8 \quad (3)$$

k_2/k_1 is listed as $C_2H_5/n\text{-}C_3H_7$ and k_3/k_1 as $n\text{-}C_3H_7/C_2H_5$.

The table is constructed with reference to the radical receiving the transferred atom. In the above example, k_2/k_1 is in the section on ethyl radicals and k_3/k_1, with the *n*-propyl radicals. The radicals are further classified according to the number of carbon atoms they contain. Thus the table starts with H atom reactions, followed by C_1 reactions (methyl radicals and halogen and oxygen containing derivatives of methyl radicals,) then by C_2 reactions, etc.

Reactants	Notes	*k*dis/*k*comb.	Temperature range	Radical source	Reference
		HYDROGEN ATOM TRANSFER			
Hydrogen atom			°*C*		
H/C_2H_5		0.05 ± 0.03	26–203	$(C_2H_5)_2CO + H_2$ −H	1
D/C_2H_5	(a)	0.21 ± 0.07	26–203	$(C_2H_5)_2CO + D_2$ −H	1
D/CH_3CD_2		0.06 ± 0.03	26–203	$(CH_3CD_2)_2CO + D_2$ −H	1
$D/i\text{-}C_3H_7$		0.2	85		2
H/C_5H_{11}		0.099	25	iso-C_5H_{12} −H	3
H/C_6H_{13}		0.12	25	$n\text{-}C_6H_{14}$ −H	4
Methyl					
$CH_3/CH_2{:}CH$		2.3	175	$CH_2{:}CHCHO$ and $HCOOCH{:}CH_2$ $+ CH_3$	5
CH_3/C_2H_5		0.04 ± 0.02	78–130	$CH_3COC_2H_5$ P	6
		0.055	77–230	$HCOOC_2H_5 + CH_3$	7
		0.039 ± 0.007	110–166	$(CH_3)_2CO + (C_2H_5)_2CO$ P	8
		0.039			
CH_3/CH_3CD_2		0.06 ± 0.01	90	$(CH_3)_2CO$ $+ (CH_3CD_2)_2CO$ P	9
CD_3/C_2H_5		< 0.08	27	$(CD_3)_2CO + (C_2H_5)_2CO$ P	10
$CH_3/n\text{-}C_3H_7$		0.095 ± 0.01	74–178	$HCOOCH_2CH_2CH_3$ $+ CH_3$	11
		0.025 ± 0.004	139–173	$n\text{-}C_3H_7CHO$ $+ CH_3$	12
		0.041 ± 0.01	118–144	$(CH_3)_2CO$ $+ (n\text{-}C_3H_7)_2N_2$ P	8
	(b)	0.14			13

Disproportionation/Combination Ratios – Continued

Reactants	Notes	kdis/kcomb.	Temperature range	Radical source	Reference
			°C		
$CD_3/CH_3CH_2CD_2$		0.05	25–28	$CD_3COCD_2CH_2CH_3$ P	14
$CH_3/i\text{-}C_3H_7$		0.216 ± 0.032	80–150	$(CH_3)_2CO + CH_3COCH(CH_3)_2$ P	15
		0.195 0.21	94–181	$HCOOCH(CH_3)_2$ + CH_3	11
CD_3/CH_3CDCH_3		0.17 ± 0.03	53–116	$CD_3COCD(CH_3)_2$ P	16
$CH_3/n\text{-}C_4H_9$		0.15	70–195	$HCOOC_4H_9$ + CH_3	13, 103
CH_3/sec-C_4H_9		0.30	−103–+25	*cis*-$CH_3CH:CHCH_3$ + H	17
		0.07	107–168	$CH_3CH:CH_2$ + CH_3	18
$CH_3/t\text{-}C_4H_9$	(c)	0.85 ± 0.1	20–60	$((CH_3)_3CO)_2$ P	19
		0.88	25–79	$((CH_3)_3CO)_2$ P	20
		0.699 ± 0.037	80–188	$((CH_3)_3C)_2CO$ P	15
	(d)	0.806 0.80			21
$CH_3/n\text{-}C_5H_{11}$		0.1	63	$CH_3COC_5H_{11}$ P	22
CD_3/cyclo-C_5H_9		0.31	132–218	$(CD_3)_2CO$ P	23
CH_3/CDO		2.5	80–180	$(CH_3)_2N_2$ P	24
CH_3/CH_3O		1.25	29	CH_3COOCH_3 P	25
	(a)	1.51 ± 0.2	124–185	CH_3OOCH_3 T	26
CH_3/CD_3O		1.4 ± 0.1	30–201	CH_3COOCD_3 P	27
CD_3/CD_3O		1.8	30–201	CH_3COOCD_3 P	27
CH_3/CH_3CO		0.06	29	CH_3COOCH_3 P	25
		0.05	30	CH_3COOCD_3 P	104
		⩽ 0.095	55	$CH_3CO.COCH_3$ − H	28
CD_3/CD_3CO		0.014 to 0.055	25	$CD_3COCD_2CH_2CH_3$ P	14
CH_3/CH_3COCH_2		0.25 ± 0.25	184–285	CH_3COCH_3 P	29
$CH_3/(CH_3)_2CHO$		3.4	26	$((CH_3)_2CHO)_2$ P	30
Methoxy					
CH_3O/CH_3O		⩾ 60	25	$(CH_3)_2N_2 + O_2$ P	31
		9.3 ± 0.6	room temp.	$CH_3I + O_2$ P	32
Halogenated Methyls					
CCl_3/C_2H_5		0.24 ± 0.04	25	$(C_2H_5)_2CO + CCl_4$ P	33
		0.22 ± 0.03	0–58	$C_2H_4 + CCl_4$ P	34
CCl_3/C_2H_4Cl		0.11 ± 0.02	26	$C_2H_4 + CCl_4$ P	105
		0.14 ± 0.03	0–58	$C_2H_4 + CCl_4$ P	34
$CCl_3/C_2H_4COC_2H_5$		0.9 ± 0.1	25	$(C_2H_5)_2CO + CCl_4$ P	33

Reactants	Notes	kdis/kcomb.	Temperature range	Radical source	Reference
			°C		
CF_2H/CF_2H		0.19	75–119	CF_2ClH −H	35
Vinyl					
$CH_2{:}CH/CH_2{:}CH$		1.1	175	$CH_2{:}CHCHO$ and $HCOOCH{:}CH_2$ $+CH_3$	5
	(e)	0.5	272–301		5
		0.02	50	$(CH_2{:}CH)_2Hg$ P	36
$CH_2{:}CH/C_2H_5$		0.03	161–175	$(C_2H_5)_2CO$ P	37
Ethyl					
$C_2H_5/CH_2{:}CH$		0.12	161–175	$(C_2H_5)_2CO$ P	37
C_2H_5/C_2H_5		0.36	75	$(C_2H_5)_2Hg$ P	38
		0.46	200	$(C_2H_5)_2Hg$ P	38
		0.11	25	$(C_2H_5)_2CO$ P	39
		0.085	101	$(C_2H_5)_2CO$ P	39
		0.17	25	C_2H_4 +H	40
		0.22–0.61	42	C_2H_4 +H	41
		0.47	200	C_2H_4 +H	41
		0.10	25	C_2H_5CHO P	42
		0.13	350	$(C_2H_5)_2Hg$ T	43
		0.13	122	C_2H_5CHO $+CH_3$	44
		0.15	156	C_2H_5CHO $+CH_3$	44
		0.13 ± 0.02	26–74	$(C_2H_5)_2N_2$ P	45
		0.12	100–200	$(C_2H_5)_2CO$ P	46
		0.15 ± 0.01	25	C_2H_4 +H	47
		0.136 ± 0.02	50–215	$(C_2H_5)_2CO$ P	48
		0.12 ± 0.01	27–118	$(C_2H_5)_2N_2$ P	49
		0.15	50–315	C_2H_5CHO P	50
		0.14	77–230	$HCOOC_2H_5$ $+CH_3$	7
	(f)	0.16 0.13 0.11_9	−65 0 40	$(C_2H_5)_2N_2$ P	51, 52
		0.130 ± 0.007	115–150	$(C_2H_5)_2CO$ P	8
		0.11 ± 0.01	22	$(C_2H_5)_2N_2$ F.P.	53
		0.123 ± 0.008	25–200	$(C_2H_5)_2CO$ P	54
		0.134 ± 0.003	79–141	$(C_2H_5)_2CO$ P	55
		0.11	room temp.	$CH_2{:}CH_2$ +H	56
		0.137	71–175	$(C_2H_5)_2CO$ P	106
		0.135			
CH_3CD_2/CH_3CD_2	(g)	0.1	24–180	$(CH_3CD_2)_2CO$ P	57
C_2D_5/C_2D_5		0.098_5 ± 0.008	50–197	$(C_2D_5)_2CO$ P	58
C_2H_5/CH_2CHCH_2		0.05	134–175	$(C_2H_5)_2CO$ P	106
$C_2H_5/n\text{-}C_3H_7$		0.14	117	$(C_2H_5)_2CO$ $+HCOOnC_3H_7$ P	59
		0.081 ± 0.01	61–129	$(C_2H_5)_2CO$ $+(n\text{-}C_3H_7)_2N_2$ P	8
		0.06 ± 0.04	−78–+24	C_3H_8 −H	60
		0.08			

Reactants	Notes	*k*dis/*k*comb.	Temperature Range	Radical Source	Reference
			°*C*		
$C_2H_5/i\text{-}C_3H_7$		0.2	room temp.	$CH_2{:}CH_2$ + $CH_3CH{:}CH_2$ +H	107
		0.21 ± 0.02	25	C_3H_8 −H	61
		0.43 ± 0.03	34–144	$HCOO\,i\text{-}C_3H_7$ + $(C_2H_5)_2CO$ P	59
		0.43	48–112	C_2H_5CHO + $i\text{-}C_3H_7CHO$ P	62
		0.43			
$C_2H_5/sec\text{-}C_4H_9$		0.23 ± 0.01	25	$n\text{-}C_4H_{10}$ −H	61
$C_2H_5/i\text{-}C_4H_9$		0.02 ± 0.02	0	$i\text{-}C_4H_{10}$ −H	60
$C_2H_5/t\text{-}C_4H_9$		0.3	room temp.	$CH_2{:}CH_2$ + $(CH_3)_2C{:}CH_2$ +H	107
		0.53	73–80	$(C_2H_5)_2CO$ + $((CH_3)_3C)_2CO$ P	62
		0.54 ± 0.01	25	$i\text{-}C_4H_{10}$ −H	61
		0.54			
$C_2H_5/cyclo\text{-}C_5H_9$		0.27 ± 0.05	25	$cyclo\text{-}C_5H_{10}$ −H	61
$C_2H_5/n\text{-}C_5H_{11}$		0.08 ± 0.04	0	$n\text{-}C_5H_{12}$ −H	60
$C_2H_5/sec\text{-}C_5H_{11}$	(h)	0.25 ± 0.01	25	$n\text{-}C_5H_{12}$ −H	61
$C_2H_5/t\text{-}C_5H_{11}$		0.60 ± 0.01	25	$(CH_3)_2CHCH_2CH_3$ −H	61
$C_2H_5/cyclo\text{-}C_6H_7$	(i)	0.38 ± 0.03	50–120	$(C_2H_5)_2CO$ P	64
$C_2H_5/(CH_3)_3CCHCH_3$		0.20 ± 0.02	25	$(CH_3)_3CCH_2CH_3$ −H	61
C_2H_5/sec-hexyl	(j)	0.27 ± 0.01	25	$n\text{-}C_6H_{14}$ −H	61
$C_2H_5/(CH_3)_2CC_3H_7$		0.74 ± 0.03	25	$(CH_3)_2CHCH_2CH_2CH_3$ −H	61
$C_2H_5/(CH_3)_2CCH(CH_3)_2$		0.72 ± 0.01	25	$(CH_3)_2CHCH(CH_3)_2$ −H	61
$C_2H_5/CH_3C(C_2H_5)_2$		0.8	25	$CH_3CH(C_2H_5)_2$ −H	61
C_2H_5/CH_3CH_2O		1.3 ± 0.2	15–29	$C_2H_5COOC_2H_5$ P	65
Ethoxy					
CH_3CH_2O/C_2H_5		2.3 ± 0.3	29	$C_2H_5COOC_2H_5$ P	65
CH_3CH_2O/CH_3CH_2O		12 ± 2	25	$C_2H_5I + O_2$ P	66
Hydroxy ethyl					
$CH_3CH(OH)/CH_3CH(OH)$	(k)	0.3	25	C_2H_5OH −H	67
Halogenated ethyl					
C_2F_5/C_2H_5		0.56	21–240	$C_2F_5COC_2H_5$ P	112
C_2H_4Cl/C_2H_5		0.22	0–58	$C_2H_4 + CCl_4$ P	34

Reactants	Notes	kdis/kcomb.	Temperature Range	Radical Source	Reference
			°C		
C_2H_4Cl/C_2H_4Cl		≤0.05	0–58	$C_2H_4+CCl_4$ P	34
		≤0.1	26	$C_2H_4+CCl_4$ P	105
	(l)	0.36	23	$C_2H_4+COCl_2$ P	68
	(m)	24	23	$C_2H_4+COCl_2$ P	68
C_2H_4Cl/C_4H_8Cl	(n)	0.40	23	$C_2H_4+COCl_2$ P	68
Allyl					
CH_2CHCH_2/C_2H_5		0.13	134–175	$(C_2H_5)_2CO$ P	106
***n*-Propyl**					
n-C_3H_7/C_2H_5		0.058±0.01	61–129	$(C_2H_5)_2CO + (n$-$C_3H_7)_2N_2$ P	8
n-C_3H_7/n-C_3H_7		0.21	113	$(n$-$C_3H_7)_2CO$ P	69
		0.1	25	n-C_3H_7CHO P	75
		0.3	30–108	$(n$-$C_3H_7)_2Hg$ P	63
		0.125±0.01	100–150	$(n$-$C_3H_7)_2CO$ P	108
		0.16	25–191	n-C_3H_7CHO P	70
		0.157	25–130	$(n$-$C_3H_7)_2N_2$ P	71
		0.14	74–178	$HCOOCH_2CH_2CH_3 + CH_3$	11
		0.141±0.015 0.14	18–150	$(n$-$C_3H_7)_2N_2$ P	8
$C_2H_5CD_2/C_2H_5CD_2$		0.15	25–28	$CH_3CH_2CD_2COCD_3$ P	14
Iso-Propyl					
iso-C_3H_7/C_2H_5		0.19	48–112	$C_2H_5CHO + i$-C_3H_7CHO P	62
		0.2	room temp.	$CH_2{:}CH_2 + CH_3CH{:}CH_2$ +H	107
		0.07 0.19	34–144	$(C_2H_5)_2CO$ P	59
iso-C_3H_7/iso-C_3H_7		1.5	30	$CH_3CH{:}CH_2$ +H	72
		2.	200	$CH_3CH{:}CH_2$ +H	72
		1.	270	$(i$-$C_3H_7)_2Hg$ T	73
		0.53	30	$(i$-$C_3H_7)_2N_2$ P	74
		0.5	25	i-C_3H_7CHO P	75
		0.77	25	$CH_3CH{:}CH_2$ +H	76
		0.48	320	$CH_3CH{:}CH_2$ +H	76
		0.6	200	$(i$-$C_3H_7)_2CO$ P	77
		0.65	20–261	i-C_3H_7CHO P	109
		0.5±0.05	room temp.	$CH_3CH{:}CH_2$ +H	56
		0.54	61–127	$((CH_3)_2CH)_2N_2$ P	78
		0.65	94–181	$HCOOi$-C_3H_7 +CH_3	11
		0.58±0.04 0.65	75–136	$((CH_3)_2CH)_2CO$ P	79
$(CH_3)_2CD/(CH_3)_2CD$		0.63±0.04	25–125	$((CH_3)_2CD)_2CO$ P	80
		0.67	53–116	$(CH_3)_2CDCOCD_3$ P	16
iso-C_3H_7/sec-C_4H_9		0.4	room temp.	$CH_3CH{:}CH_2 + CH_3CH{:}CHCH_3$ +H	107

Disproportionation/Combination Ratios – Continued

Reactants	Notes	kdis/kcomb.	Temperature Range	Radical Source	Reference
			°C		
iso-C_3H_7/t-C_4H_9		0.5	room temp.	$CH_3CH{:}CH_2$ + $(CH_3)_2C{:}CH_2$ + H	107
		0.70	72–82	$(t\text{-}C_4H_9)_2CO$ + $(i\text{-}C_3H_7)_2CO$ P	62
iso-C_3H_7/cyclo-C_6H_7	(i)	0.52 ± 0.09	75–136	$(i\text{-}C_3H_7)_2CO$ P	79
Propoxy					
C_2H_5CO/C_2H_5		0.4 ± 0.1	24	$(C_2H_5)_2CO$ FP	81
***n*-Perfluoropropyl**					
n-C_3F_7/C_2H_5		0.40	87–196	$(n\text{-}C_3F_7)_2CO$ P	82
	(o)	0.021 exp (2.2/RT)	80–256	n-$C_3F_7COC_2H_5$ P	83
Butyls					
n-C_4H_9/n-C_4H_9		5.	140	$(n\text{-}C_4H_9)_2Hg$ P	84
		0.94 ± 0.05	70–195	HCOOn-C_4H_9 + CH_3	13
		0.95 ± 0.05	75–186	HCOOn-C_4H_9 + CH_3	103
	(p)	$10^{0.6}$ exp (−1.3/RT) 0.95	61–229	n-C_4H_9CHO P	15
sec-C_4H_9/i-C_3H_7	(r)	0.4	room temp.	$CH_3CH{:}CH_2$ + $CH_3CH{:}CHCH_3$ + H	107
sec-C_4H_9/sec-C_4H_9	(q)	1.64	25	$CH_3CH_2CH(CH_3)CHO$ P	85
		2.27	100	$(CH_3CH_2CH(CH_3))_2CO$ P	86
		1.5	room temp.	$CH_3CH{:}CHCH_3$ + H	110
		0.95	−103–+25	cis$CH_3CH{:}CHCH_3$ + H	17
		≤ 1.2	107–168	$CH_3CH{:}CH_2$ + CH_3	87
		1.5	24	$CH_3CH_2CH{:}CH_2$ + H	84
		3.5	220	$CH_3CH_2CH{:}CH_2$ + H	84
		0.63 ± 0.08	−78–+25	trans-$CH_3CH{:}CHCH_3$ + H	88
sec-C_4H_9/t-C_4H_9	(r)	0.23	room temp.	$CH_3CH{:}CHCH_3$ + $(CH_3)_2C{:}CH_2$ + H	107
iso-C_4H_9/iso-C_4H_9		0.42	78–109	$((CH_3)_2CHCH_2)_2CO$ P	86
		0.17 0.17	26–124	$(CH_3)_2CHCH_2CHO$ P	89
t-C_4H_9/C_2H_5	(r)	1.7	room temp.	$CH_2{:}CH_2$ + $(CH_3)_2C{:}CH_2$ + H	107
		0.31	73–80	$(t\text{-}C_4H_9)_2CO$ + $(C_2H_5)_2CO$ P	62
t-C_4H_9/iso-C_3H_7	(r)	1.2	room temp.	$CH_3CH{:}CH_2$ + $(CH_3)_2C{:}CH_2$ + H	107
		0.67	72–82	$(t\text{-}C_4H_9)_2CO$ + $(i\text{-}C_3H_7)_2CO$ P	62

Disproportionation/Combination Ratios – Continued

Reactants	Notes	$k$dis/$k$comb.	Temperature Range	Radical Source	Reference
			°C		
$t\text{-}C_4H_9/sec\text{-}C_4H_9$	(r)	2.0	room temp.	$CH_3CH{:}CHCH_3 + (CH_3)_2C{:}CH_2$ +H	107
$t\text{-}C_4H_9/t\text{-}C_4H_9$		4.5	23	$(CH_3)_2C{:}CH_2$ +H	84
		6.5	300	$(CH_3)_2C{:}CH_2$ +H	84
		4.59	117–322	$(t\text{-}C_4H_9)_2CO$ P	86
		7.4	20–60	$(t\text{-}C_4H_9O)_2$ P	90
		4.38	27–230	$t\text{-}C_4H_9CHO$ P	91
		3.19	50–80	$(t\text{-}C_4H_9)_2CO$ and $t\text{-}C_4H_9CHO$ P	62
		2.2 ± 0.3	room temp.	$(CH_3)_2C{:}CH_2$ +H	107
		3.2			
Monochlorobutyl					
C_4H_8Cl/C_2H_4Cl		0.07	23	$CH_2{:}CH_2 + COCl_2$ P	68
Pentyls					
$n\text{-}C_5H_{11}/n\text{-}C_5H_{11}$		0.2	63	$n\text{-}C_5H_{11}COCH_3$ P	22
C_5H_{11}/C_5H_{11}		2.45	25	iso-C_5H_{12} −H	3
		≥ 0.66	21	$n\text{-}C_5H_{12}$ −H	92
cyclo-C_5H_9/cyclo-C_5H_9		0.19	29	cyclo-C_5H_{10} −H	93
		1.0	24	cyclo-C_5H_{10} −H	94
		1.0	26–250	cyclo-C_5H_{10} −H	95
		1.0			
Hexyls					
cyclo-C_6H_{11}/cyclo-C_6H_{11}		0.46	29	cyclo-C_6H_{12} −H	111
cyclo-C_6H_{11}/cyclo-C_6H_{11}	(s)	0.42	29		93
C_6H_{13}/C_6H_{13}		0.97 ± 0.08	25	$n\text{-}C_6H_{14}$ −H	4
Amino					
NH_2/NH_2		0.18	no indication	NH_3 F.P.	97
Nitric Oxide					
NO/CH_3O	(t)	0.5	174		96
NO/CH_3CH_2O		0.28	95–135	$(C_2H_5O)_2$ P	96
$NO/(CH_3)_2CHO$	(u)	{0.15	26		30
		0.175	79	$(i\text{-}C_3H_7O)_2$ P	30
Iodine atom					
I/C_2H_5		0.33 ± 0.03	28	$(C_2H_5)_2CO + C_2H_5I$ P	98

CHLORINE ATOM TRANSFER

Reactants	Notes	$k$dis/$k$comb.	Temperature Range	Radical Source	Reference
Halogenated Methyl					
CF_2Cl/CF_2Cl		≤ 0.5	75–119	CF_2ClH −H	99

Disproportionation/Combination Ratios—Continued

Reactants	Notes	kdis/kcomb.	Temperature Range	Radical Source	Reference
			°C		
Halogenated Ethyl					
C_2H_4Cl/C_2H_4Cl		≤0.1	26	$C_2H_4+CCl_4$ P	105
	(m)	5.8	23	$C_2H_4+COCl_2$ P	68
$C_2F_2Cl_3/C_2F_2Cl_3$		≤0.13	30–70	$CF_2{:}CCl_2+Cl_2$ P	100
C_2H_4Cl/C_4H_8Cl	(n) (v)	0.5	23	$C_2H_4+COCl_2$ P	68
Monochlorobutyl					
C_4H_8Cl/C_2H_4Cl	(n) (w)	4.0	23	$C_2H_4+COCl_2$ P	68
		OXYGEN ATOM TRANSFER			
Methyl					
CH_3/NO_2		2.0	55–90	$CH_3CHO+NO_2$	101
	(x) (y)	2.4	25	CH_3NO_2 P	102
	(x) (y)	1.8	105	CH_3NO_2 P	102

Notes

(a) Authors consider this value to be too high.
(b) Unpublished work by Thynne.
(c) Author believes the radicals to be vibrationally exited.
(d) A recalculation of data from Kerr and Trotman-Dickenson, J. Chem. Soc. 1609 (1960).
(e) Calculated from data of Le Roy and Tickner, J. Chem. Phys. **19**, 1247 (1951).
(f) The temperature dependence gives either *E*dis-*E*comb $=-0.3$ kcal/mole or *k*dis/*k*comb$=T^{-0.7}$.
(g) The ethylene formed was more than 90 percent $C_2H_2D_2$.
(h) *Sec*-pentyl is a mixture of the radicals $CH_3CH_2CHCH_2CH_3$ and $CH_3CHCH_2CH_2CH_3$.
(i) *Cyclo*-C_6H_7 is the cyclohexadienyl-1,4 radical.
(j) *Sec*-hexyl is a mixture of the radicals $CH_3CH{-}C_4H_9$ and $C_2H_5CHC_3H_7$.
(k) This value is probably low.
(l) Combination product is 1.4–$C_4H_8Cl_2$.
(m) Combination product is 1.3–$C_4H_8Cl_2$.
(n) Combination product is 1.6–$C_6H_{12}Cl_2$.
(o) Alternatively *k*dis/*k*comb$=0.33$ with a large scatter.
(p) Temperature coefficient very doubtful.
(q) In the range 25–243 °C, the results fit the expression *k*dis/*k*comb$=0.715$ exp (500/RT).
(r) Very doubtful.
(s) *Cyclo*-C_6H_{11} is the methylcyclopentanyl radical.
(t) Unpublished work by Phillips.
(u) The ratio could be 0.16 within the experimental error of both results.
(v) Products of the disproportionation reaction are C_4H_8 and 1,2-$C_2H_4Cl_2$.
(w) Products of the disproportionation reaction are C_2H_4 and 1,4-$C_4H_8Cl_2$.
(x) The "disproportionation reaction" is the sum of the rate constants for two reactions viz. (i) $CH_3+NO_2=CH_3ONO$, and (ii) $CH_3+NO_2=CH_3O+NO$.
(y) Combination product is CH_3NO_2.

References

(1) Heller and Gordon, J. Chem. Phys. **36,** 2648 (1962).
(2) Heller and Gordon, J. Phys. Chem. **64,** 390 (1960).
(3) Kuntz, J. Phys. Chem. **69,** 2291 (1965).
(4) Kuntz, J. Phys. Chem. **69,** 4396 (1965).
(5) Weir, J. Chem. Soc. 6870 (1965).
(6) Ausloos and Steacie, Can. J. Chem. **33,** 1062 (1955).
(7) Thynne, Trans. Faraday Soc. **58,** 676 (1962).
(8) Grotewold and Kerr, J. Chem. Soc. 4337 (1963).
(9) Heller, J. Chem. Phys. **28,** 1255 (1958).
(10) Wijnen, J. Chem. Phys. **22,** 1631 (1954).
(11) Thynne, Trans. Faraday Soc. **58,** 1394 (1962).
(12) Grotewold and Kerr, J. Chem. Soc. 4342 (1963).
(13) Thynne, Proc. Chem. Soc. 18 (1961).
(14) Ausloos and Murad, J. Am. Chem. Soc. **80,** 5929 (1958).
(15) Kerr and Trotman-Dickenson, J. Chem. Soc. 1609 (1960).
(16) Heller, J. Chem. Phys. **35,** 1711 (1961).
(17) Rabinovitch and Diesen, J. Chem. Phys. **30,** 735 (1959).
(18) Miyoshi and Brinton, J. Chem. Phys. **36,** 3019 (1962).
(19) Frey, Proc. Chem. Soc. 385 (1959).
(20) McMillan, J. Am. Chem. Soc. **82,** 2422 (1960).
(21) Blake, Henderson, and Kutschke, Can. J. Chem. **39,** 1920 (1961).
(22) Wijnen, J. Am. Chem. Soc. **83,** 3752 (1961).
(23) Gordon, Can. J. Chem. **43,** 570 (1965).
(24) Toby and Kutschke, Can. J. Chem. **37,** 672 (1959).
(25) Wijnen, J. Chem. Phys. **27,** 710 (1957).
(26) Thynne and Gray, Trans. Faraday Soc. **59,** 1149 (1963).
(27) Wijnen, J. Chem. Phys. **28,** 939 (1958).
(28) Harrison and Lossing, Can. J. Chem. **37,** 1478 (1959).
(29) Darwent, Allard, Hartman, and Lange, J. Phys. Chem. **64,** 1847 (1960).
(30) McMillan, J. Am. Chem. Soc. **83,** 3018 (1961).
(31) Dever and Calvert, J. Am. Chem. Soc. **84,** 1362 (1962).
(32) Heicklen and Johnston, J. Am. Chem. Soc. **84,** 4030 (1962).
(33) Gregory and Wijnen, J. Chem. Phys. **38,** 2925 (1963).
(34) Rocquitte and Wijnen, J. Am. Chem. Soc. **85,** 2053 (1963).
(35) Bellas, Strausz, and Gunning, Can. J. Chem. **43,** 1022 (1965).
(36) Sherwood and Gunning, J. Phys. Chem. **69,** 2323 (1965).

(37) James and Troughton, Trans. Faraday Soc. **62,** 145 (1966).
(38) Ivin and Steacie, Proc. Roy. Soc. **208A,** 25 (1951).
(39) Kutschke, Wijnen, and Steacie, J. Am. Chem. Soc. **74,** 714 (1952).
(40) Moore and Taylor, J. Chem. Phys. **8,** 504 (1940).
(41) Le Roy and Khan, J. Chem. Phys. **15,** 816 (1947).
(42) Blacet and Pitts, J. Am. Chem. Soc. **74,** 3382 (1952).
(43) Gowenlock, Polanyi, and Warhurst, Proc. Roy. Soc. **218A,** 269 (1953).
(44) Volman and Brinton, J. Chem. Phys. **22,** 929 (1954).
(45) Ausloos and Steacie, Bull. Soc. Chim. Belges. **63,** 87 (1954).
(46) Brinton and Steacie, Can. J. Chem. **33,** 1840 (1955).
(47) Smith, Beatty, Pindar, and Le Roy, Can. J. Chem. **33,** 821 (1955).
(48) James and Steacie, Proc. Roy. Soc. **244A,** 289 (1958).
(49) Cerfontain and Kutschke, Can. J. Chem. **36,** 344 (1958).
(50) Kerr and Trotman-Dickenson, J. Chem. Soc. 1611 (1960).
(51) Dixon, Stefani, and Szwarc. J. Am. Chem. Soc. **85,** 2551 (1963).
(52) Matsuoka, Dixon, Stefani, and Szwarc, Proc. Chem. Soc. 304 (1962).
(53) Dingledy and Calvert, J. Am. Chem. Soc. **85,** 856 (1963).
(54) Brown and James, Can. J. Chem. **43,** 660 (1965).
(55) James and Troughton, Trans. Faraday Soc. **62,** 120 (1966).
(56) Boddy and Robb, Proc. Roy. Soc. **249A,** 518 (1959).
(57) Wijnen and Steacie, Can. J. Chem. **29,** 1092 (1951).
(58) Boddy and Steacie, Can. J. Chem. **38,** 1576 (1960).
(59) Thynne, Proc. Chem. Soc. 68 (1961).
(60) Holroyd and Pierce, J. Phys. Chem. **68,** 1392 (1964).
(61) Holroyd and Klein, J. Phys. Chem. **67,** 2273 (1963).
(62) Dominguez, Kerr, and Trotman-Dickenson, J. Chem. Soc. 3357 (1962).
(63) Caule and Steacie, Can. J. Chem. **29,** 103 (1951).
(64) Brown and James, Can. J. Chem. **43,** 660 (1965).
(65) Wijnen, J. Am. Chem. Soc. **82,** 3034 (1960).
(66) Heicklen and Johnston, J. Am. Chem. Soc. **84,** 4030 (1962).
(67) Knight and Gunning, Can. J. Chem. **39,** 2466 (1961).
(68) Heicklen, J. Am. Chem. Soc. **87,** 445 (1965).
(69) Masson, J. Am. Chem. Soc. **74,** 4731 (1952).
(70) Kerr and Trotman-Dickenson, Trans. Faraday Soc. **55,** 572 (1959).
(71) Kerr and Calvert, J. Am. Chem. Soc. **83,** 3391 (1961).
(72) Moore, J. Chem. Phys. **16,** 916 (1948).
(73) Chilton and Gowenlock, Trans. Faraday Soc. **49,** 1451 (1953).
(74) Durham and Steacie, Can. J. Chem. **31,** 377 (1953).
(75) Blacet and Calvert, J. Am. Chem. Soc. **73,** 661 (1951).
(76) Hoey and Le Roy, Can. J. Chem. **33,** 580 (1955).
(77) Heller and Gordon, J. Phys. Chem. **60,** 1315 (1956).
(78) Riem and Kutschke, Can. J. Chem. **38,** 2332 (1960).
(79) James and Suart, J. Am. Chem. Soc. **86,** 5424 (1964).
(80) Heller and Gordon, J. Phys. Chem. **62,** 709 (1958).
(81) Fischer and Mains, J. Phys. Chem. **68,** 188 (1964).
(82) Giacometti and Steacie, Can. J. Chem. **36,** 1493 (1958).
(83) Pritchard and Thommarson, J. Phys. Chem. **69,** 1001 (1965).
(84) Moore and Wall, J. Chem. Phys. **17,** 1325 (1949).
(85) Gruver and Calvert, J. Am. Chem. Soc. **78,** 5208 (1956).
(86) Kraus and Calvert, J. Am. Chem. Soc. **79,** 5921 (1957).
(87) Miyoshi and Brinton, J. Chem. Phys. **36,** 3019 (1962).
(88) Kubin, Rabinovitch, and Harrington, J. Chem. Phys. **37,** 937 (1962).
(89) Metcalfe and Trotman-Dickenson, J. Chem. Soc. 5072 (1960).
(90) Frey, Proc. Chem. Soc. 385 (1959).
(91) Birrell and Trotman-Dickenson, J. Chem. Soc. 4218, (1960).
(92) Back, Trans. Faraday Soc. **54,** 512 (1958).
(93) Beck, Kniebes, and Gunning, J. Chem. Phys. **22,** 678 (1954).
(94) Stock and Gunning, Can. J. Chem. **38,** 2295 (1960).
(95) Gunning and Stock, Can. J. Chem. **42,** 357 (1964).
(96) Arden, Phillips, and Shaw, J. Chem. Soc. 5126 (1964).
(97) Salzman and Bair, J. Chem. Phys. **41,** 3654 (1964).
(98) Guercione and Wijnen, J. Chem. Phys. **38,** 1 (1963).
(99) Bellas, Strausz, and Gunning, Can. J. Chem. **43,** 1022 (1965).
(100) Vallana, Castellano, and Schumacher, Z. Phys. Chem. **46,** 294 (1965).
(101) Phillips and Shaw, 10th Int. Comb. Symp., p. 423, Combustion Institute, Pittsburgh (1965).
(102) Rebbert and Slagg, Bull. Soc. Chim. Belges **71,** 709 (1962).
(103) Thynne, Trans. Faraday Soc. **58,** 1533 (1962).
(104) Wijnen, J. Chem. Phys. **28,** 271 (1958).
(105) Roquitte and Wijnen, J. Chem. Phys. **38,** 4 (1963).
(106) James and Troughton, Trans. Faraday Soc. **62,** 145 (1966).
(107) Boddy and Robb, Proc. Roy. Soc. **249A,** 547 (1959).
(108) Whiteway and Masson, J. Chem. Phys. **25,** 233 (1956).
(109) Kerr and Trotman-Dickenson, Trans. Faraday Soc. **55,** 921 (1959).
(110) Boddy and Robb, Proc. Roy. Soc. **249A,** 532 (1959).
(111) Beck, Kniebes, and Gunning, J. Chem. Phys. **22,** 672 (1954).
(112) Thommarson and Pritchard, J. Phys. Chem. **70,** 2307 (1966).

Molecule-Molecule Reactions (Hydrogen and Hydrogen Halides)

Reactions	Notes	E	$\log_{10}A$	Temperature range	Radical source	Reference
		(kcal mole⁻¹)	*(cm³ mole⁻¹ sec⁻¹)*	°C		
$H_2+O_2=2OH$		45.0	($k=84.0$)	485	H_2/O_2 ignition	1
		67.0	14.4	687–807	H_2/O_2 S.T.	2
$H_2+I_2=2HI$	(a)	39.0	14.1	10–235	HI T	3
		41.0	15.09	598–774	H_2/I_2 T	9, 10
			$k=6.60\pm0.09$	394	H_2/I_2 T	11
		41.24 ± 0.25	14.35 ± 0.07	105–360	H_2/I_2 T	12
$D_2+I_2=2DI$	(b) (c)	41.47 ± 0.20	14.14 ± 0.07	360–465	D_2/I_2 T	13
$H_2^p+HI=H_2^o+HI$		44 ± 3	13.7	420–480	$H_2/I_2/HI$ T	14
		$\geqslant 47$		420–480	$H_2/I_2/HI$ T	17
$H_2+NO_2=NO+H_2O$		18	9.3	384–434	$H_2/O_2/NO_2$ T	15
$HCl+NO_2=HNO_2+Cl$		23.4	11.6	100–420	HCl/NO_2 T	23
$HBr+NO_2=HNO_2+Br$		13.0	11.0	180–310	HBr/NO_2 T	23
$HBr+C_2F_4=C_2F_4Br+H$		54.6	16.96	858–1013	$H_2/O_2/C_2F_4Br_2$ S.T.	22
$2HI=H_2+I_2$	(d) (a)	44.0	13.9	10–235	HI T	3
		49.2	15.56	597–774	HI T	9, 10
		44.20 ± 0.25	13.54 ± 0.07	105–360	H_2/I_2 T	12
$HI+CH_3I=CH_4+I_2$	(e)	33.4	14.3	270–320	CH_3I/HI T	19
$DI+CH_3I=CH_3D+I_2$			$k=1.54$	250	$CH_3I/HI/DI$ T	20
$HI+C_2H_5I=C_2H_6+I_2$	(e)	29.8	13.7	250–300	C_2H_5I/HI T	19
$HI+n\text{-}C_3H_7I=C_3H_8+I_2$	(e)	19.2	14.1	260–300	$n\text{-}C_3H_7I/HI$ T	19

Ratios of Rate Constants

Reactions	Notes	E_1-E_2	$\log_{10}A_1/A_2$	k_1/k_2	Temperature range	Radical source	Reference
		(kcal mole⁻¹)			°C		
(1) $HBr+CH_2N_2=CH_3Br+N_2$ (2) $HCl+CH_2N_2=CH_3Cl+N_2$		−1.5	−0.091		−78–27	$CH_2N_2/HBr/HCl$ T	21
(1) $HI+CH_2N_2=CH_3I+N_2$ (2) $HBr+CH_2N_2=CH_3Br+N_2$				4 ± 2	27	$CH_2N_2/HI/HBr$ T	21
(1) $HI+CH_2N_2=CH_3I+N_2$ (2) $HCl+CH_2N_2=CH_3Cl+N_2$				50 ± 15	27	$CH_2N_2/HI/HCl$ T	21

Notes

(a) These values summarise a considerable body of early data (references 4 to 8).

(b) For data on the reaction $HD + I_2 = HI + DI$, see reference 16.

(c) For a summary of early data see reference 3.

(d) For data on the reaction $2DI = D_2 + I_2$ see references 13 and 18.

(e) The *A* factor values originally reported (reference 19) are too large by a factor of ten (reference 20).

References

1. Semenov, Acta Physicochimica U.S.S.R. **20,** 291 (1945).
2. Skinner and Ringrose, J. Chem. Phys. **42,** 2190 (1965).
3. Trotman-Dickenson, "Gas Kinetics," p. 255 et seq. (Butterworths, London, 1955).
4. Bodenstein, Z. Phys. Chem. **13,** 56 (1894).
5. Bodenstein, Z. Phys. Chem. **22,** 1 (1897).
6. Bodenstein, Z. Phys. Chem. **29,** 295 (1899).
7. Kassel, Proc. Nat. Acad. Sci. Wash. **16,** 358 (1930).
8. Kistiakowsky, J. Am. Chem. Soc. **50,** 2315 (1928).
9. Graven, J. Am. Chem. Soc. **78,** 3297 (1956).
10. Horie, Ishii, and Amano, J. Phys. Chem. **68,** 1264 (1964).
11. Sullivan, J. Chem. Phys. **36,** 1925 (1962).
12. Sullivan, J. Chem. Phys. **30,** 1292 (1959).
13. Sullivan, J. Chem. Phys. **39,** 3001 (1963).
14. Steiner, Trans. Faraday Soc. **36,** 1111 (1940).
15. Crist and Wertz, J. Chem. Phys. **7,** 719 (1939).
16. Magee, J. Am. Chem. Soc. **79,** 5375 (1957).
17. Sullivan, J. Chem. Phys. **30,** 1577 (1959).
18. Taylor and Crist, J. Am. Chem. Soc. **63,** 1377 (1941).
19. Ogg, J. Am. Chem. Soc. **56,** 526 (1934).
20. Newton, J. Chem. Phys. **18,** 797 (1950).
21. Hassler and Setser, J. Am. Chem. Soc. **87,** 3793 (1965).
22. Skinner and Ringrose, J. Chem. Phys. **43,** 4129 (1965).
23. Rosser and Wise, J. Phys. Chem. **64,** 602 (1960).

Molecule–Molecule Reactions (Hydrocarbons and Hydrocarbon Derivatives)

Reactions	Notes	E	$\log_{10} A$	Temperature range	Radical source	Reference
Alkanes		*(kcal mole⁻¹)*	*(cm³ mole⁻¹ sec⁻¹)*	°C		
$CH_4 + O_3 =$ products		15.35	11.21	35–64	$CH_4/O_3/O_2$ T	1
		13.90	11.15	35–64	CH_4/O_3 T	1
$C_2H_6 + C_2H_4 = 2C_2H_5$		68.9	17.6	752–917	$H_2/O_2/C_2H_4$ S.T.	2
Alkenes and aromatics						
CH_2:CHCH:CH_2 $+ C_2N_2 = H_2 +$ 2-cyano pyridine		31.6	12.20	325–450	C_2N_2/C_4H_6 T	3
CH_2:CHCH:CH_2 $+ CF_3CN = H_2 +$ 2-trifluoromethyl pyridine		21.5	9.32	350–520	CF_3CN/C_4H_6 T	4
CH_2:CHCH:CH_2 $+ CF_3CF_2CN = H_2$ + 2-pentafluoroethyl pyridine		25.0	10.42	340–460	C_2F_5CN/C_4H_6 T	5
CH_2:CHCH:CH_2 $+ CF_3CF_2CF_2CN$ $= H_2 +$ 2-perfluoropropyl pyridine		25.8	10.51	340–460	C_3F_7CN/C_4H_6 T	5
$2C_6H_6 = C_{12}H_{10} + H_2$		40	14.0	900–1210	C_6H_6 T	6
Alkynes						
$2C_2H_2 =$ products	(b)	50.2	16.57	352–472	C_2H_2 T	7
$2C_2H_2 = C_4H_2 + H_2$	(b)	~ 30			C_2H_2 S.T.	8
$2C_2H_2 = C_4H_2 + H_2$	(b)	36.4 ± 3	12.89	1127–2227	C_2H_2 S.T.	9
$2C_2H_2 = C_2H_2^* + C_2H_2$	(b)	50	14.04	1227–2227	C_2H_2 S.T.	10
$2C_2H_2 = C_4H_3 + H$	(b)	38.8 ± 7.5	13.47 ± 0.78	1630–1922	C_2H_2 S.T.	11
	(a)	41.6 ± 0.6	13.77 ± 0.11	347–2177		11
Hydrocarbon derivatives						
$CH_3CHO + O_2$ $= HO_2 + CH_3CO$		29 ± 2		320–380	CH_3CHO/O_2 T	12
$CH_3I + I^* - I$ $= CH_3I^* + I_2$	(c)	9.0	6.40	60–140	CH_3I/I_2 T	13
$CH_3OCH_3 + NO$ $= HNO$ $+ CH_2OCH_3$		43.4	14.0	500–600	CH_3OCH_3/NO T	14

Notes

(a) Critical review of literature data.

(b) These values are included in the review estimate (a), the products of the reaction being considered to be $C_4H_3 + H$.

(c) These values may be low because of complicating heterogeneous reactions.

References

1. Dillemuth, Skidmore, and Schubert, J. Phys. Chem. **64**, 1496 (1960).
2. Skinner and Ringrose, J. Chem. Phys. **43**, 4129 (1965).
3. Hawkins and Janz, J. Am. Chem. Soc. **74**, 1790 (1952).
4. Jarvie and Janz, J. Phys. Chem. **60**, 1430 (1956).
5. Monahan and Janz, J. Phys. Chem. **69**, 1070 (1965).
6. Hou and Palmer, J. Phys. Chem. **69**, 863 (1965).
7. Silcocks, Proc. Roy. Soc. **242A**, 411 (1957).
8. Greene, Taylor, and Patterson, J. Phys. Chem. **62**, 238 (1958).
9. Aten and Greene, Comb and Flame **5**, 55 (1961).
10. Palmer and Dormish, J. Phys. Chem. **68**, 1553 (1964).
11. Gay, Kistiakowsky, Michael, and Niki, J. Chem. Phys. **43**, 1720 (1965).
12. Sokolova, Markevich, and Nalbandyan, Russ. J. Phys. Chem. (Eng. Trans.) **35**, 415 (1961).
13. Schmied and Fink, J. Chem. Phys. **27**, 1034 (1957).
14. McKenney, Wojciechowski, and Laidler, Can. J. Chem. **41**, 1993 (1963).

Molecule–Molecule Reactions Involving Nitric Oxide

Reaction	Notes	E	$\log_{10} A$	Temperature range	Radical source	Reference
		(*kcal mole*$^{-1}$)	(*cm*^{3} *mole*$^{-1}$ *sec*$^{-1}$)	°C		
$NO + CH_3OCH_3 = HNO + CH_2OCH_3$		43.4	14.0	500–600	CH_3OCH_3/NO T	1
$NO + CCl_3CHO = HNO + CCl_3CO$		37.1	13.5	356–421	CCl_3CHO/NO T	20, 21
$NO + F_2 = ONF + F$		1.5 ± 1.0	11.78	−78–+27	NO_2/F_2 D.F.	2
$NO + XeF_4 = ONF + XeF_3$		7 to 9		27–77	XeF_4/NO T	3
$NO + XeF_2 = ONF + XeF$		10 to 12		27–77	XeF_4/NO T	3
$NO + Cl_2 = NOCl + Cl$		$k = (2.7 \pm 1.0) \times 10^2$		158	NOCl T	4
		$k = (8.3 \pm 3.0) \times 10^2$		178		
		$k = (10.0 \pm 4.0) \times 10^2$		198		
	(b)	20.3	12.6	25–55		18
$NO + NO_2Cl = NO_2 + NOCl$		6.9	11.92	1–71	NO_2Cl/NO T	19
$NO + O_3 = NO_2 + O_2$		2.5 ± 0.3	11.90	−75–−43	NO/O_3 T	5
		$k = 3 \times 10^{10}$		29	NO/O_3 T	6
	(a)	2.55 ± 0.22	12.08	−28–+78	NO/O_3	7
		$k = 7.6 \times 10^9$		60	NO/O_3 T	8
		$k = 1.5 \times 10^{10}$		25	NO_2/O_2 discharge	9
		$k = (1.26 \pm 0.30) \times 10^{10}$		25	O_3/N_2 discharge	10
		2.46 ± 0.15	11.76	−57–+49	NO/O_3 T	11
$NO + NO = N_2 + O_2$		63.8	12.42	1062–1257	NO T	12, 13
		63.1	13.49	1400–1800	NO T	14
		57.0	12.91	2730–4030	NO S.T.	15
$NO + N_2O = N_2 + NO_2$		50.0	14.3	1227–1927	NO/N_2O S.T.	16
		50.0	14.4	700–760		17
$CH_3CH_2O^{15}NO + {}^{14}NO = CH_3CH_2O^{14}NO + {}^{15}NO$		21.4 ± 0.5	11.48	130–150	$CH_3CH_2O^{15}NO/{}^{14}NO$ T	22
$CF_3CH_2O^{15}NO + {}^{14}NO = CF_3CH_2O^{14}NO + {}^{15}NO$		23.7 ± 0.5	12.78	130–150	$CF_3CH_2O^{15}NO/{}^{14}NO$ T	22

Notes

(a) Reaction carried out using supersonic nozzle technique.
(b) Estimated from the reverse reaction.

References

1. McKenney, Wojciechowski, and Laidler, Can. J. Chem. **41,** 1993 (1963).
2. Rapp and Johnston, J. Chem. Phys. **33,** 695 (1960).
3. Johnston and Woolfolk, J. Chem. Phys. **41,** 269 (1964).
4. Ashmore and Spencer, Trans. Faraday Soc. **55,** 1868 (1959).
5. Johnston and Crosby, J. Chem. Phys. **22,** 689 (1954).
6. Ford, Doyle, and Endow, J. Chem. Phys. **26,** 1337 (1957).
7. Marte, Tschuikow-Roux, and Ford, J. Chem. Phys. **39,** 3227 (1963).
8. Borok, Zhur. Fiz. Khim. **35,** 2275 (1961).
9. Phillips and Schiff, J. Chem. Phys. **37,** 924 (1962).
10. Phillips and Schiff, J. Chem. Phys. **36,** 1509 (1962).
11. Clyne, Thrush, and Wayne, Trans. Faraday Soc. **60,** 359 (1964).
12. Kaufman and Kelso, J. Chem. Phys. **23,** 1702 (1955).
13. Kaufman and Decker, 7th Int. Comb. Symp., p. 57 (Butterworths, London, 1959).
14. Yuan, Slaughter, Koerner, and Daniels, J. Phys. Chem. **63,** 952 (1959).
15. Freedman and Daiber, J. Chem. Phys. **34,** 1271 (1961).
16. Fishburne and Edse, J. Chem. Phys. **41,** 1297 (1964).
17. Kaufman and Kelso, J. Chem. Phys. **23,** 602 (1955).
18. Ashmore and Chanmugam, Trans. Faraday Soc. **49,** 270 (1953).
19. Freiling, Johnston, and Ogg, J. Chem. Phys. **20,** 327 (1952).
20. Verhoek, Trans. Faraday Soc. **31,** 1521 (1935).
21. Trotman-Dickenson, "Gas Kinetics," p. 212 (Butterworths, London, 1955).
22. Kuhn and Günthard, Helv. Chim. Acta. **43,** 607 (1960).

247-168 O-67—9

Nitrogen Dioxide (Molecule–Molecule Reactions)

Reactions	Notes	E	$\log_{10} A$	Temperature range	Radical source		Reference
		(kcal mole⁻¹)	*(cm³ mole⁻¹ sec⁻¹)*	°C			
$NO_2 + H_2 = NO + H_2O$		18.	9.3	384–434	$H_2/O_2/NO_2$	T	19
$NO_2 + HCHO = HNO_2 + HCO$		15.1	10.1	118–160	$HCHO/NO_2$	T	20
$NO_2 + CHOCHO = HNO_2 + COCHO$		19.8	11.9	160–210	$CHOCHO/NO_2$	T	21
$NO_2 + CH_3CHO = HNO_2 + CH_3CO$		16.0	12.9	118–143	CH_3CHO/NO_2	T	22
$NO_2 + NH_3 = HNO_2 + NH_2$		27.5	12.7	327–527	NH_3/NO_2	T	1
$NO_2 + HCl = HNO_2 + Cl$		23.4	11.6	100–420	HCl/NO_2	T	2
$NO_2 + HBr = HNO_2 + Br$		13.0	11.0	180–310	HBr/NO_2	T	2
$NO_2 + F_2 = NO_2F + F$		10.5	12.2	28–70	NO_2/F_2	T	7
$NO_2 + F_2O = NO_2F + FO$		14.48	11.11	60–80	F_2O/NO_2	T	18
$NO_2 + Cl_2O = NO_2Cl + OCl$		11.6	10.64	20–60	NO_2/Cl_2O	T	3
$NO_2 + ClO_2 = NO_3 + OCl$		11.5	10.68				3
$NO_2 + NOCl = NO + NO_2Cl$		10.0	10.28	−20–+8	$NOCl/ClO_2$	T	4
$NO_2 + CO = CO_2 + NO$		31.6	13.08	267–454	CO/NO_2	T	5
		27.8	11.68	225–290	CO/NO_2	T	6
$NO_2 + O_3 = NO_3 + O_2$		7.0	12.77	13–29	O_3/NO_2	T	8
			$k = 1.96 \times 10^7$	room temp.	O_3/NO_2	T	9
$2NO_2 = NO + NO_3$			$k = 2.6 \times 10^4$	434	NO_2	T	10
		23.90 ± 0.60	11.89 ± 0.25	200–430	NO_2	T	11
	(a)	23.					12
$2NO_2 = 2NO + O_2$	(b)	27.10	12.69	320–380	NO_2	T	13, 11
		26.90	12.60	357–747	NO_2	T	14, 11
		26.90 ± 0.10	12.60 ± 0.04	200–550	NO_2	T	11, 10
$2NO_2 =$ products	(c)	25.6	11.8	319–383			15
	(c)	25.0 ± 5.0	13.40	1127–2027	NO_2	S.T.	16
	(c)	25.7	12.95	1227–1827	NO_2	S.T.	17

Notes

(a) Estimated from the reverse reaction.

(b) These values were recalculated from the original data (reference 11).

(c) These values represent the sums of the contributions from $2NO_2 = 2NO + O_2$ and $2NO_2 = NO + NO_3$.

References

1. Rosser and Wise, J. Chem. Phys. **25,** 1078 (1956).
2. Rosser and Wise, J. Phys. Chem. **64,** 602 (1960).
3. Martin, Meise, and Engelmann, Z. Phys. Chem. **24,** 285 (1960).
4. Martin and Kohnlein, Z. Phys. Chem. **17,** 375 (1958).
5. Johnston, Bonner, and Wilson, J. Chem. Phys. **26,** 1002 (1957).
6. Brown and Crist, J. Chem. Phys. **9,** 840 (1941).
7. Perrine and Johnston, J. Chem. Phys. **21,** 2202 (1953)
8. Johnston and Yost, J. Chem. Phys. **17,** 386 (1949).
9. Ford, Doyle, and Endow, J. Chem. Phys. **26,** 1336 (1957).
10. Ashmore and Levitt, Research **9,** s25 (1956).
11. Ashmore and Burnett, Trans. Faraday Soc. **58,** 253 (1962).
12. Schott and Davidson, J. Am. Chem. Soc. **80,** 1841 (1958).
13. Bodenstein and Ramstetter, Z. Phys. Chem. **100,** 106 (1922).
14. Rosser and Wise, J. Chem. Phys. **24,** 493 (1956).
15. Kassel, "The Kinetics of Homogeneous Gas Reactions," p. 156 (Chemical Catalog Co., N.Y., 1932).
16. Huffman and Davidson, J. Am. Chem. Soc. **81,** 2311 (1959).
17. Fishburne, Bergbauer, and Edse, J. Chem. Phys. **43,** 1847 (1965).
18. De Staricco, Sicre, and Schumacher, Z. Phys. Chem. **39,** 337 (1963).
19. Crist and Wertz, J. Chem. Phys. **7,** 719 (1939).
20. Pollard and Wyatt, Trans. Faraday Soc. **45,** 760 (1949).
21. Thomas, Trans. Faraday Soc. **49,** 630 (1953).
22. McDowell and Thomas, Trans. Faraday Soc. **46,** 1030 (1950).

Molecule–Molecule Reactions (Inorganic Molecules)

Reactions	Notes	E	$\log_{10} A$	Temperature range	Radical source	Reference
		(kcal mole⁻¹)	*(cm³ mole⁻¹ sec⁻¹)*	°C		
$F_2 + CO = FCO + F$		13.5 ± 1.2	11.67	15–45	$F_2/CO/O_2$ T	1, 2
$F_2 + ClO_2 = FClO_2 + F$		8.5 ± 0.4	10.6	−46–−26	F_2/ClO_2 T	3
		8.0 ± 0.5	10.11	−46–−26	F_2/ClO_2 T	4
$Cl_2 + O_3 = ClO + ClO_2$		26.0 ± 1		35–60	Cl_2/O_3 T	5
$2ClCN = Cl_2 + C_2N_2$		60.	13.	1727–2527	ClCN S.T.	6
$2NOCl = Cl_2 + 2NO$		23.4	12.5	150–250		7
		23.6 ± 0.7	12.7 ± 0.3	150–411	NOCl T	8
$2NOI = I_2 + 2NO$			$k \leqslant 4 \times 10^{10}$	60	NO/I_2 F.P.	15
$2O_3 = 3O_2$		18.8	12.65	70–100	O_3 T	9
$CO + O_2 = CO_2 + O$		51.0 ± 7.0	12.54 ± 0.22	2127–2727	CO/O_2 S.T.	10
$CO + B_2H_6 = BH_3 + BH_3CO$	(a)	17.65	11.32	0–60		11
$BF_3 + BCl_3 = BF_2Cl + BFCl_2$			$k \approx 5 \times 10^3$	23	BF_3/BCl_3 T	12
$PH_3 + B_2H_6 = PH_3BH_3(g) + BH_3$		11.4	9.5	−24–0	PH_3/B_2H_6 T	14, 13, 11

Notes

(a) Critical review of literature data.

References

1. Heras, Arvia, Aymonino, and Schumacher, Anales Asoc. Quim. Argentina **50,** 120 (1962).
2. Heras, Arvia, Aymonino, and Schumacher, Z. Phys. Chem. N.F. **28,** 250 (1961).
3. Aymonino, Sicre, and Schumacher, J. Chem. Phys. **22,** 756 (1954).
4. Aymonino, Sicre, and Schumacher, Anales Asoc. Quim. Argentina **43,** 26 (1955).
5. Schumacher, Z. Phys. Chem. **13,** 353 (1957).
6. Schofield, Tsang, and Bauer, J. Chem. Phys. **42,** 2132 (1965).
7. Ashmore and Spencer, Trans. Faraday Soc. **55,** 1868 (1959).
8. Ashmore and Spencer, Trans. Faraday Soc. **58,** 1801 (1962).
9. Pshezhetskii, Morozov, Kamenetskaya, Sirystskaya, and Bribova, Zhur. Fiz. Khim. **33,** 2306 (1959).
10. Sulzmann, Myers, and Bartle, J. Phys. Chem. **42,** 3969 (1965).
11. Garabedian and Benson, J. Am. Chem. Soc. **86,** 176 (1964).
12. Nightingale and Crawford, J. Chem. Phys. **22,** 1468 (1954).
13. Bauer, J. Am. Chem. Soc. **78,** 5775 (1956).
14. Brumberger and Marcus, J. Chem. Phys. **24,** 741 (1956).
15. Porter, Szabo, and Townsend, Proc. Roy. Soc. **270A,** 493 (1962).

Termolecular Reactions

Reactions	Notes	E	$\log_{10}A$	Temperature range	Radical source	Reference
		(*kcal mole*$^{-1}$)	(*cm*^{6} *mole*$^{-2}$ *sec*$^{-1}$)	°C		
$2NO + O_2 = 2NO_2$	(a)		$k = (7.45 \pm 0.22) \times 10^9$	25	NO/O_2 T	1
			$k = 6.0 \times 10^9$	25	NO/O_2 T	2
			$k = 7.10 \times 10^9$	25	NO/O_2 T	3
$2NO + Cl_2 = 2NOCl$	(b)	4.2	10.4			8, 9
		6.0	11.4	100–250	NO/Cl_2 T	10
$2NO + Br_2 = 2NOBr$		1.6	10.6	−8–15	NO/Br_2 T	11, 8
$2NO + H_2 =$ products	(c)	47	18.7	700–825	NO/H_2 T	12, 8
$NO + NO_2 + O_2 = NO_2 + NO_3$			$k = 6.58 \times 10^7$	25	$NOCl/NO_2/O_2$ T	13
	(d)		$k = 3.0 \times 10^7$			15
		−0.96	7.32	200–430	NO_2 T	14
$2NO_2 + O_2 = 2NO_3$	(e)	25	($k = 7 \times 10^{-12}$)	27		15
$H + O_2 + H_2 = H_2O + OH$			$k = 2 \times 10^{11}$	830–1630	H_2/O_2 S.T.	16
$CF_3NO + 2NO = CF_3 + N_2 + NO_3$			$k = 5.6 \times 10^5$	24	CF_3I/NO P	17
$CH_3NO + 2NO = CH_3 + N_2 + NO_3$	(f)	−1.8	6.41	25–70	CH_3I/NO P	18
$C_2H_5NO + 2NO = C_2H_5 + N_2 + NO_3$	(f)	−2.9	6.28	25–70	C_2H_5I/NO P	18
$CH_3CH_2CH_2NO + 2NO = CH_3CH_2CH_2 + N_2 + NO_3$	(f)	−7	3.7	25–45	C_3H_7I/NO P	18
$(CH_3)_2CHNO + 2NO = (CH_3)_2CH + N_2 + NO_3$	(f)	−4	5.3	25–45	$(CH_3)_2CHI/NO$ P	18
$(CH_3)_3CNO + 2NO = (CH_3)_3C + N_2 + NO_3$	(f)	−7.5		25–70	$(CH_3)_3CI/NO$ P	18

Notes

(a) Further data on this reaction can be found in references 4 to 7.

(b) Critical survey of literature data. The Arrhenius plot is curved, and the values given are valid only at low temperatures.

(c) It is unlikely that the nitric oxide-hydrogen reaction is a simple termolecular process.

(d) Temperature independent. Estimated from the reverse reaction.

(e) Estimated from the reverse reaction.

(f) These values are for an overall reaction which could be $RNO + NO \rightleftharpoons R(NO)_2$; $R(NO)_2 + NO = R + N_2 + NO_3$.

References

1. Brown and Crist, J. Chem. Phys. **9,** 840 (1941).
2. Smith, J. Am. Chem. Soc. **65,** 74 (1943).
3. Johnston and Slentz, J. Am. Chem. Soc. **73,** 2948 (1951).
4. Bodenstein and Lindner, Z. Phys. Chem. **100,** 87 (1922).
5. Bodenstein and Wachenheim, Z. Electrochem. **24,** 183 (1918).
6. Matthes, Miss Dissertation Berlin, 1933, quoted by Schumacher "Chemische Gasreaktion," p. 314 (Steinhopff, Dresden, 1938).
7. Briner, Pfeiffer, and Malet, J. Chim. Phys. **21,** 25 (1924).
8. Trotman-Dickenson, "Gas Kinetics," p. 265 (Butterworths, London, 1955).
9. Welinsky and Taylor, J. Chem. Phys. **6,** 466 (1938).
10. Ashmore and Spencer, Trans. Faraday Soc. **55,** 1868 (1959).
11. Krauss, Z. Phys. Chem. **175A,** 295 (1936).
12. Hinshelwood and Mitchell, J. Chem. Soc. 378 (1936).
13. Ray and Ogg, J. Chem. Phys. **29,** 984 (1957).
14. Ashmore and Burnett, Trans. Faraday Soc. **58,** 253 (1962).
15. Schott and Davidson, J. Am. Chem. Soc. **80,** 1841 (1958).
16. Belles and Lauver, J. Chem. Phys. **40,** 415 (1964).
17. Heicklen, J. Phys. Chem. **70,** 112 (1966).
18. Christie, Foot, and Voisey, Trans. Faraday Soc. **61,** 674 (1965).

Inversion (Group Transfer) Reactions

Reactions	Notes	E	$\log_{10}A$	Temperature range	Radical source	Reference
		(kcal mole^{-1})	(cm^3 mole^{-1} sec^{-1})	°C		
$^{14}CH_3 + CH_3COCH_3 = {}^{14}CH_3COCH_3 + CH_3$	(a)	$k = 5.2 \times 10^6$		350	CH_3COCH_3 P	1
$CH_3 + CF_3COCF_3 = CH_3COCF_3 + CF_3$		5.7 ± 1.5	9.3	163–245	$CH_3N_2CH_3$ P and T	2
		6.2 ± 1.0	11.4	85–210	CF_3COCF_3 P	3
		7.0 ± 1.0	11.7	48–240	CH_3COCH_3/ CF_3COCF_3 P	4
$CH_3 + C_2F_5COC_2F_5 = CH_3COC_2F_5 + C_2F_5$		7 ± 1		184–240	$(C_2F_5)_2CO$ P	5
$CD_3 + CH_3HgCH_3 = CD_3HgCH_3 + CH_3$		$k = 8.9 \times 10^5$		180	CD_3COCD_3 P	6, 7
$CH_3 + CD_3SH = CH_3SH + CD_3$		7.6	10.73	130–200	CH_3COCH_3 P	8
$CH_3 + CF_3COCH_3 = C_2H_6 + CF_3CO$		14.		150–350	CF_3COCH_3 P	9
$CH_3 + CH_3COCOCH_3 = CH_3COCH_3 + CH_3CO$		5.6	10.7	100–200	$CH_3COCOCH_3$ P	10
		6.6		100–200	$CH_3COCOCH_3$ P	11
$CH_3 + CH_3CH{:}CHCHO = CH_3CH{:}CHCH_3 + CHO$		7.45 ± 1.30	11.8 ± 0.4	120–250	CH_3COCH_3 P	12
$CH_3 + CH_3HgCH_3 = C_2H_6 + (Hg + CH_3)$		1.0	7	175–220	$(CH_3)_2Hg$ P	13, 14
$C_6H_5 + C_6H_5COCH_3 = C_6H_5C_6H_5 + CH_3CO$	(b)	6.2	9.6	277–407	$C_6H_5COCH_3$ P	15
$CF_3CH_2O^{15}NO + {}^{14}NO = CF_3CH_2O^{14}NO + {}^{15}NO$		23.7 ± 0.5	12.78	130–150	$CF_3CH_2O^{15}NO/{}^{14}NO$ T	16
$CH_3CH_2O^{15}NO + {}^{14}NO = CH_3CH_2O^{14}NO + {}^{15}NO$		21.4 ± + 0.5	11.48	130–150	$CH_3CH_2O^{15}NO/{}^{14}NO$ T	16
$BH_3 + B_2D_6 = BH_3BD_3 + BD_3$		6.0	14.2	24–44	B_2H_6/B_2D_6 T	17, 14, 21, 22
		7.8	13.45			18
$BH_3 + BH_3CO = B_2H_6 + CO$		7.0	11.4	0–30	BH_3CO T	19, 17, 22
$PH_3 + B_2H_6 = BH_3PH_3 + BH_3$		11.4 ± 2	9.5	−24–0		20, 22

Notes

(a) Assuming $k = 10^{11.6}$ exp $(-9800/RT)$ for the reaction $CH_3 + CH_3COCH_3 = CH_4 + CH_2COCH_3$.

(b) C_6H_5 refers to the phenyl radical.

References

1. Dainton, Ivin, and Wilkinson, Trans. Faraday Soc. **55**, 929 (1959).
2. Pritchard and Steacie, Can. J. Chem. **35,** 1216 (1957).
3. Alcock and Whittle, Trans. Faraday Soc. **61,** 244 (1965).
4. Giles and Whittle, Trans. Faraday Soc. **61,** 1425 (1965).
5. Price and Kutschke, Can. J. Chem. **38,** 2128 (1960).
6. Rebbert and Ausloos, J. Am. Chem. Soc. **86,** 2068 (1964).
7. Rebbert and Ausloos, J. Am. Chem. Soc. **85,** 3086 (1963).
8. Greig and Thynne, Trans. Faraday Soc. **62,** 379 (1966).
9. Sieger and Calvert, J. Am. Chem. Soc. **76,** 5197 (1954).
10. Blacet and Bell, Disc. Faraday Soc. **14,** 70 (1953).
11. Bell and Blacet, J. Am. Chem. Soc. **76,** 5332 (1954).
12. Allen and Pitts, J. Phys. Chem. **70,** 1691 (1966).
13. Gomer and Noyes, J. Am. Chem. Soc. **71,** 3390 (1949).
14. Trotman-Dickenson, "Gas Kinetics," p. 237 et seq. (Butterworths, London, 1955).
15. Duncan and Trotman-Dickenson, J. Chem. Soc. 4672 (1962).
16. Kuhn and Gunthard, Helv. Chim. Acta. **43,** 607 (1960).
17. Bauer, Shepp, and McCoy, J. Am. Chem. Soc. **75,** 1003 (1953).
18. Roth and Bauer, 5th Int. Comb. Symp., p. 710 (Reinhold, New York, 1955).
19. Burg, J. Am. Chem. Soc. **74,** 3482 (1952).
20. Brumberger and Marcus, J. Chem. Phys. **24,** 741 (1956).
21. Maybury and Koski, J. Chem. Phys. **21,** 742 (1953).
22. Garabedian and Benson, J. Am. Chem. Soc. **86,** 176 (1964).

U. S. GOVERNMENT PRINTING OFFICE : 1967 OL—247-168

(cut here)

Announcement of New Publications on Standard Reference Data

Superintendent of Documents,
Government Printing Office,
Washington, D.C. 20402

Dear Sir:

Please add my name to the announcement list of new publications to be issued in the series: National Standard Reference Data Series—National Bureau of Standards.

Name____

Company______________________________________

Address______________________________________

City________________State______________Zip Code______________

(Notification Key N337)